HESSLE ROAD SCALLYWAGS

The Hessle Road Scallywags

Ian Achmed AKA Ian Achmed Newton
Jimmy Turner (Nickname Isse)
Terry Cox
Frankie Callis

Front cover illustration by Kevin Ward,
A Hessle Roader from Havelock Street

FROM THE BESTSELLING AUTHOR OF 'DUSTBINGATE'

IAN NEWTON

First published in Great Britain in 2013 by Riverhead
Second edition printed in 2014

A CIP catalogue record for this book is
available from the British Library

ISBN 978-0-9567782-6-0

Design and Production by Riverhead, Hull
44-46 High Street, Hull, East Yorkshire. HU1 1PS
Telephone: 01482 318218
email: mike@riverheadbooks.karoo.co.uk

Printed by: Fisk Printers, Hull

Dedication

This book is dedicated to my long-suffering wife Jennifer,
who has put up with my eccentric 'past times' for so long.
Also to my son Andrew Newton Lee, who found a sponsor
for this book.
And to my mother Nora Lillian Newton,
who died on Saturday May 5th 2012 at 09.40pm
after a long and difficult journey through life.

The author wishes to appologise for any distress caused by comments
made in the first edition and consequently some names have been
removed.

Acknowledgements

My thanks go to

My classmates from Year One, Daltry Street Infants School 1960.

Other books by:

Other books by Ian Newton
Dustbingate
Pizza Wars
The Night Shift

INTRODUCTION
Just food for thought and a rant.

In the fast moving and insecure times in which we live today, I suppose many of us suffering the mental turmoil and confusion of "middle age, old codgers syndrome" hanker back to the warmer and more secure times of our childhood for refuge and comfort. With today's almost unlimited supply of digital television channels, many of us afflicted with the melancholy of middle age have almost instant access to programmes like Steptoe and Son, On The Buses or Please Sir, with many more available on DVD. In many ways the old goggle box in the corner has become a bit like our own old fart's Tardis but with one difference, our Tardis only travels back in time. And to tell you the truth, with the present day as it is, almost too much to handle for many like me, who wants to travel into the future? To see yourself slumped in the corner of some tatty local authority residential home, dribbling and having your incontinence pad changed by some hot young female care assistant, indifferently man-handling you as she gossips to her friends about the amazing sex she had on a binging Saturday one-night-stand. By that time God only knows what morality will be left in society, since there is hardly any left now and I wonder what new levels of depravity television will have sunk to by then in East Enders and Coronation Street. I'm sure on Emmerdale that the scriptwriters are feverishly plotting as we speak to weave in a much bigger and more intimate part for Billy The Goat as a new love interest of Samantha. Yet they still won't be showing Love Thy Neighbour or Till Death Us Do Part on UK Gold. Bring back Annie Sugden I say. She will sort out all the mucky goings-on in the village. If you are like me, you will probably have little or no time, or understanding even, for today's so-called sit-coms or the politically correct humour that pervades our TV screens and now oppresses almost all aspects of our daily lives in what seems to be an increasingly humourless society.

My own answer to this dilemma is a simple one. I find it is just so easy to put on the television and slip in a DVD collection of golden oldie TV programmes and let my memories happily roll back the years.

With the secret agents of the politically correct "Thought Police" in every office and on every factory floor, just waiting and yearning to be offended, so that they can rush off with an attack of the vapours to the boss's office, or contact some ambulance-chasing solicitor for deliverance from injustice. Not to mention of course, the hope of getting a big fat dirty wad of cash for the psychological damage. We are a society that is frightened to laugh, on pain of losing our job. Big Brother is indeed watching you. It is hard not to conclude that there is indeed some underhand, sinister war of destruction going on to annihilate British working class culture and that the main purveyors are our own morally bankrupt and corrupt political classes. What of course they don't understand is that all the humour of our class, which they do not approve of in their feckless minds has gone underground and your mates send it in e-mails or to your mobile phone. Our politicians should take note and great care, because underground movements have a habit of becoming the revolutions of the future and as history has shown so many times, politicians of such periods of betrayal, have been known to end up hanging from lampposts and we all live in hope.

In these tedious and burdening times I find it soothing, more than is healthy as my wife so often tells me, to watch a great deal of old TV programmes that were popular in my childhood.

With a bottle of vodka and a bottle of soda close at

hand - and a fag- shhhh - I slowly become lost in them as the anaesthetic effects of the vodka kick in. And I find myself wishing a door would open to the past and I could step through and see my old friends again from Hessle Road one last time before I kick the bucket and maybe relive some of the fun we had together.

As I have become terminally pissed off with the endless numbers of such graphic murders, sex, bad language and bloody "celebrity" shite programmes that pervade the TV. And equally the number of infinite and bloody shite digital TV channels, I have taken to buying old TV programmes on DVDs. My house is full of them but please don't tell the "The Politically Correct Thought Police". How right George Orwell was in his book 1984. The only thing he got wrong it seems was the date and then not by that far.

The old TV programmes I am talking about are not just old TV programmes to my generation but trusty old friends. Many of them conjure up memories of both friends and events from childhood, not just for me but for millions of other old complaining sods of my age. In middle age there is a tendency to fear change and to become grumpy old farts, moaning about immigration, dodgy politicians and bankers, you name it and I think at this moment in time, more than any before, we have very good reason to. I have to admit, like many of my age, I do not like the times I am living in and the way the country is changing. I have no wish to become judgemental in my "middle age crisis years", as I am aware that as all generations merrily dance through their years to the old wooden box waiting at the end of life's bumpy road to nowhere, almost everybody gets to the "middle age grumpy phase" of hating almost anything new. If we look back I cannot really think of a time when we were totally free of an economic crisis or the fear of being swamped by foreigners. Yes, it has all happened before and no doubt we will struggle through, get depressed and think often of suicide but be too scared to do it in case we injure ourselves and end up as a cabbage on a life support machine or even worse, living on disability benefit on a sink council estate with a house full of dolies, chavs or hoodies next door. If none of those options takes your fancy you could always run for Parliament and become an M.P., especially if you're a cabbage because that does seem to be one of the basic entry requirements, as well as being able to read and write so you can legally fiddle your taxes and expenses. I don't suppose it would matter if you ran as a Labour, Conservative or Liberal because as my old Gran used to say, "They all piss in the same pot." And as an "honourable" M.P. you only need to be focused on one real burning issue and that is to look after your own interests, and tax to death, toll or fine anybody who works hard.

By now you have probably gleaned from the tone of my writing that I am not a great lover of those who exercise power over us and consequently I find myself often thinking deeply about the times we live in and pondering where the world will end up. But let's not get too deep or my next ramblings will sound like the prophecies of Nostradamus and what with the vodka, that's a slippery slope at my age. Even so I have to admit that as I look back on my own youth and compare it to the present day, I can see that on many occasions my generation also did equally distasteful things as today's youth. We were just as rebellious, challenging and probably more mischievous in our pursuit of fun. And we were a lot braver because back then there were serious consequences and serious punishments for what are now considered misdemeanours. Unlike today, where even a hint of the word "punishment" sends some bleeding heart Liberal on a rant about Human Rights for all except ordinary working Joe, who cannot afford to enforce his human rights because he is unfortunate enough to be working and because he is not a locked up murderer or child molester, and does not qualify for legal aid. How times change but we should not

8

despair because given human history, the pendulum, I am sure will swing back as it always does.

Even though I bemoan the immorality of our times, I do freely admit an element of hypocrisy in my rants because I am sure in the heady days of my youth my mates and I got our fair share of sex commensurate with the times. But to make a sociological observation as social worker and social scientist, I would say that girls from my era did not seem to drop their knickers as eagerly as they do today. I'm not sure here if I'm complaining but let us move on. There was also not much we would not do for a good laugh, no matter who suffered or what damage we did. As I slide slowly to oblivion one of the few things that does bring a smile to my face is my childhood days on Hessle Road and I think about them more and more as time relentlessly marches on. I do have regrets about some of the things I did as both a child and a teenager and looking back some of our antics may have gone too far. But on the whole I think most of it was merely extremely mischievous fun and I cannot remember anybody getting physically hurt by us. The sense of right and wrong was very clear cut when I was growing up in the 1950s and there was no room for confusion.

In my day there were only two major influences in your life and they were your parents, or in my case parent and the school. These imparted to you your values and your sense of right and wrong, and boundaries though regularly crossed and challenged were very clear cut and almost black and white and ignorance was absolutely no excuse. If you got caught it was always, "A fair cop Gov." and they did not spare the rod. As children then, unlike today, we did not have a daily barrage of thousands of signals bombarding us from TV, film, radio, thousands of glossy magazines, chav celebrity culture and of course the infinite internet. Now, literally anything goes and literally anything is available, from Transsexual ballroom dancing Rumanian midgets, to any sexual and social perversion you could ever want, if you are so inclined. It is very easy to understand why youngsters today are so confused about morality and right and wrong, as there are way too many signals for them to understand, let alone cope with.

Although I admit that in my day I might have been considered a troublemaker and a rebel, mainly due to being marginalised because of my ethnic origins. That aside, I come from a British generation where hard work was considered a virtue. It was a time when the country manufactured real things and industry and your job was the bedrock of social life. Whether a poor man or a rich man, children were surrounded by positive role models we could look up to and respect, like teachers, police officers and those stalwart volunteers who ran the evening boxing clubs and evening play centres. When my mates and me were doing wrong, we knew we were doing wrong and we knew the consequences. Today it all seems to have gone wrong and excuses abound for all manner of wrongdoing. Consequently our society's moral foundations are crumbling and the great industrial foundations of Britain have been exchanged for the fool's gold of financial services and the insidious and massive rise of gambling and its promotion, along with the now all pervading sex and alcohol industry. All these together are creating yet more own goals in the form of self-inflicted social problems and addictions, to be added to the many others already blighting our communities. It is one of the greatest ironies I encounter as a social worker almost every day, that most of the problems in society I come across are man manufactured. And they have only become a problem because politicians have deliberately turned a blind eye to the blindingly obvious consequences so that their rich friends can make a fast buck.

Sometimes it often feels like being under financial siege and that you cannot even pick up the phone and ring your doctor without being ripped off on a premium rate telephone line. Everywhere a rip off seems to be hiding around the corner. The hidden scourge of arrangement and cancellation fees for this or that, fly around like confetti and where once a bank or building society was content to make a profit from their interest charges they have now found the golden goose of the "hidden charge" or "the small print". Pure greed now reigns supreme and rules go unchallenged as the ordinary working man finds his pocket picked almost everyday. Inevitably common sense tells us it cannot go on. But the faults in society, so obvious at ground level, appear to be invisible or more likely simply ignored by our institutionally corrupt rulers and power brokers who become ever more decadent and oblivious to what is happening at society's core.

For many of today's younger generation there are virtually no positive role models anywhere but lots of negative ones. Everybody from the top of society to the bottom seems to be on the fiddle with only hardworking, ordinary Joe sandwiched in the middle and haplessly banging away on the treadmill of life, whilst being fleeced by a taxman on the orders of our inglorious politicians. They in turn complain endlessly about their now curtailed expenses whilst earning £65,000 a year plus junkets and all the other outside fiddles they can get away with. It is due to them in no small measure that today there is no sense of community and we tend to live our lives in a bubble looking out for number one. Many of us – who work that is - a dying breed, find our lives so busy with the intense routines of life that we have little time to think, let alone consider others. As a social worker I work constantly with an endless and ever growing number of dysfunctional families and cannot help but agree with the comparison that gradually the entire British nation is slowly becoming one big dysfunctional family. A family becomes dysfunctional usually because of dysfunctional parents and the learned behaviours passed on from parents to children. Similarly, a nation becomes dysfunctional as those who rule it become decadent and corrupt and so set the standards for the rest of us. I cannot remember who said this - I can really but he's a Tory and I hate to quote a privileged old Etonian establishment toff - but he famously described Britain as "Broken". Whilst he may have just been looking for a snappy sound bite, no one could have put it more succinctly and so aptly in just one word, "Broken" and I am not hopeful it can be fixed by the morally deficient mob that are our political establishment.

"If there is something wrong with your government there is usually something wrong with the people," it was once said, well visa versa. Alistair Cook in his famous letters from America once said, "When nations become obsessed with sex, greed, materialism and violence it hails the dawn of the beginning of the end." Today all these four are in the ascendency in our society and there is a smell of fire that Rome is starting to burn once more, whilst across the European Union in the halls of power, champagne is being poured at great feasts whilst fiddles are being played. The period of terminal decadence seems to be upon us and no doubt our times will be added to the dust of hundreds of great civilisations that came before. Because after all, are we really so arrogant as to believe that our times are so special that we can escape the natural cycle that has ended greater civilisations than ours?

I think not. Rant over. I never would have made a very good warm up act for the King's comedian but what the hell.

Now let's get in our Tardis, forget all our troubles for a short while and have a really good laugh as we travel back in time down old Hessle Road. Let's steal someone's bike, knock on some old git's door at midnight and generally do some really evil stuff that kids in those days loved to do to pass the time...

CHAPTER ONE

Down Hessle Road where I grew up and specifically in my case down Marmaduke Street, one way or another we were all in the same boat. Nobody seemed to have much money and many of the families usually survived from week to week borrowing money off neighbours to get through the week, if not there was always "the slate" at the corner shop. The older I get the more those long gone times haunt me. The friends I had, the fun we had and the absolute array of colourful and hilarious characters that lived on Hessle Road and in particular that lived down Marmaduke Street, where I spent six of the happiest and funniest years of my life. No matter who you are, if you live in Hull, you will no doubt be aware that of all the places in the city, Hessle Road seems to hold a special place, not only in the minds of Hull people but also for local historians, writers and TV documentary makers. They have all tried to capture the mystery of why Hessle Road was and still is so special, and so extra special to those who like me were brought up there.

At 56 years old - Oh God, am I really that old? - I often look back and think about my childhood years. And with every bloody birthday and Christmas that comes round - and comes round apparently so fast that it seems like only yesterday that you took the Asda ready-made Christmas tree down – then with the blink of an eye its Christmas groundhog day again! When you're a kid time seems to move so slowly, Christmas seemed to take ages coming.

I remember my first day starting infants at Daltry Street School like it was yesterday. All the new starters like me walked in all coy and bashful and as our mothers left one by one the artificial smiles left the teachers' faces just as quickly and we were all dragged down the corridor screaming and crying. I absolutely hated it and the day seemed to drag on forever. Was I glad when it was over and that bell rang to go home and I skipped down the road like a spring lamb after leaving that school hand in hand with my Mum.

"Did you like school then?" she asked me.

"It was alright," I answered with a cocky voice, "But I'm glad it's over, phew I couldn't do that every day."

I suppose like many of my age we wonder where the years have gone and gone so quickly. It's strange and a little scary when you have more years behind you than are left in front of you. Suddenly you become painfully aware that you are mortal, that you are going to get old and decrepit and then kids will be knocking on your door and running away and calling you a miserable old git. Then one day you will be dead and buried in some overgrown graveyard that in ten years will be bulldozed and used for Barrett houses.

My mother does not help matters, every time I go around she can't wait to tell me who is dead. She sits there like the Grim Reaper reading the 'deaths' column of the Hull Daily Mail. My wife's mother is the same only she goes one better and will ring you up and give you a running commentary on who has popped their clogs. She'll be using text messages soon. Thank God she doesn't know how to use Facebook – yet.

You always know when my mother is about to put you on a downer, you go into her flat all happy because you have managed to fiddle some extra hours overtime and you have decided to treat your old mum with your little windfall to some groceries. Before you even get your backside on a chair, she suddenly puts on a big dramatic voice, which always starts with a big, "Ooooh! Did you see who was in the deaths yesterday? You remember that Trevor so-and-so? He lived down Walcott Street, you know who I mean, his mother was on the game?"

Well fancy that, his mother being on the game. I don't know what that had to do with old Trevor popping off but it does throw light on why he always had the latest football boots whilst the rest of us played in those cheap two-bob black plastic boots from Boyes. And then good old mum would announce, "He was only your age, you know," and give me that long searching stare over her glasses, as if weighing up my chances of getting out of her flat without keeling over from a heart attack. Her words hung in the air like the toll of the death bell and she stared at me again. Well thanks for that mother, I feel much better now, why take the Prozac when I can talk to you?

I always have luck like that with people from my past on Hessle Road, not only my mum. This is the God's honest truth. Every year for the past five years on the run up to Christmas I always seem to bump into this old friend from Daltry Street infant school from my Hessle Road days. I can never remember his name and am too polite to ask since he remembers mine. So during our elongated one way conversation I answer by calling him, Mate, as you do, it's an easy get-out. I have not seen him for umpteen years and suddenly there he is every Christmas, his smiling face beaming through the crowds of happy Christmas shoppers. There is no stopping him, he's like a guided missile as he homes in on me and our lass and cuts his way through the crowds to get to us. I may be getting paranoid but I'm sure he plans it. I should qualify something here and I hope you won't think too badly of me, when I say he was a friend because I may be exaggerating just a little bit to compensate for my guilt. In those days, he was more of a pastime really. He was the one in the class you always picked on if you were bored. He always had a snotty nose, never seemed to get washed and smelt worse than I imagined Steptoe's horse would. No one would ever sit with him in class and he had a sort of invisible exclusion zone around him to protect us from the smell. He was the one who always got his name called out after the 'Dick nurse' had been and would come back stinking of dick lotion. I am sure you are getting my drift now. I remember my mates and me seemed to spend an awful lot of time ducking his head down the school toilets at playtime. Looking at him now, his luck doesn't seem to have changed much and he still seemed to have an aversion to washing and cleaning what few black teeth he has left. I am not trying to be bitchy here, just trying to conjure up a picture for you. I often feel guilty as he talks to me and although he never says anything, I always get the feeling he's thinking about what we used to do to him and that he would love to smack me in the nose. But we're all grown up now and that was just kids stuff. 'Auld Lang Syne' and all that.

Anyway I don't want to get distracted again but just put the record straight. As I said I have bumped into him for the past five Christmases and he goes over the same old stuff every year and seems to take a grim pleasure informing me year on year and adding to the roll call of dead and luckless from our school years. I am beginning to think he is the Ghost of Christmas Past and is haunting me for my sins.

"Ooooooh, did you hear about, Peter so-and-so," he starts up all wide-eyed and lips all dramatically puckered up like some gossiping old woman. "He's dead you know, do you remember Paul so-and-so, terrible about him getting run over and did you hear about Mary so-and-so, it was in all the papers, stabbed her husband. And what about Graham so-and-so, got life for murder, and Colin so-and-so, he set alight to those houses and murdered that woman."

I have used the term so-and-so in surnames here to

be polite and considerate to any surviving relatives and that is only right. It's only natural to want to be sensitive and that aside I know of one former classmate who was an arsonist and is out now and I have no wish to be woken by a midnight postman pouring petrol through my letterbox after reading this book. I do though know exactly what you are thinking, I seem to have gone to school with a lot of "to be" murderers and children who would grow up and blossom into generally nasty people. I often think that but I became a social worker and after thirty years of marriage I only think about murder. Anyway this bloke is the 'Angel of Death' and the legendary 'Bird of Ill Omen' rolled into one. I don't think I have bumped into him once in the past five years and been told any good news. I mean you don't need it do you at that time of the year. You have just spent hours with your lass dragging you round the shops, you're tired, cold, and hungry and your arms are dropping off with carrying the heavy bags of Christmas shopping. And she is trying on yet another pair of jeans that are too tight for her, that make her arse look fat and that would be far better suited to a girl of twenty. I am seriously thinking of wearing a false beard next Christmas when I go shopping with our lass in an attempt to avoid him.

I thought maybe this year whilst Christmas shopping fate had maybe conspired to let me off the hook. Thank you God. I had been in town several times shopping with our lass with no blip on my mental radar of the 'Hessle Road Grinch'. I managed to get all the way to Christmas Eve, the last day's shopping, actually made it into St.Stephen's car park and got all the shopping into the boot. I started the car and our lass lit a cig, which is always a good sign that she is satisfied with emptying my wallet. But then she pipes up, "I forgot the bread."

"We'll go to Asda at Kingswood," I answered casually.

"No," our lass demanded. "By the time those

Bransholme Christmas shite hawks have finished they'll be nothing left." You wouldn't think we used to live on Bransholme would you, our lass has become quite nouveau riche since moving onto Kingswood, which is known locally as "Posh Bransholme". Anyway, she demanded we go back into St. Stephen's Tesco and get some bloody bread. Arguing with our lass is like banging your head against a brick wall, all you get is a headache and if you carry it on you will just find yourself on a GBH charge. So off we toddled back into Tesco with me muttering under my breath like Mutley the dog. Got the bread, treated myself to a chocolate doughnut and was just merrily eating it when out of nowhere outside of Tesco, there he is waiting to pounce, a mental scream of horror goes through my head, It's Dr Death! He seemed to walk towards me in slow motion, like 'horrors' do in bad dreams. He was the type of bloke that lets Jehovah's Witnesses in, if you know what I mean?

"Hello Ian, fancy seeing you again." That's all I needed with the mood I was in but it was Christmas so I did try.

"Oh hiya, you alright mate?" I knew asking would tempt fate.

"Not been really, been ever so ill, lost me mother in June and me Uncle Billy died a month ago."

"Nothing serious I hope," I answered clumsily, "You being ill I mean, not your mum dying. Sorry to hear about your Mum."

"Oh she had a good innings, so she couldn't complain. You know I nursed her day and night and she went in her sleep, God bless. Her last night we must have talked all night about the old days down Hessle Road. Her last words to me were, "Son I just can't take it anymore.""

I knew exactly how she bloody felt and I bet on the death certificate it said cause of death, "bored to death." Anyway he still continued onward relentlessly. "Oh but

18

my Uncle Billy went terrible towards the end. Blocked up terrible, couldn't piss, couldn't shit and when he could shit, it was so loose it just came away from him."

There was really no answer to that, except to throw away my chocolate doughnut, there was no stopping him now.

"You remember my Uncle Billy, he sailed with your Uncle Jimmy." My Uncle Jimmy was a well-known cook and general piss-head on the trawlers in Hull. Also I had absolutely no idea who the hell his Uncle Billy was but under the circumstances of him being dead like, it seemed more respectful just to go along with the conversation.

"Oh yeah, real nice bloke Billy."

"No, you're thinking of me Uncle Ted, Uncle Billy was a miserable old sod."

I asked for that really. "Oh that's who I meant Ted." I was buggered if I knew who he was either but in for a penny and I started to edge away. "Anyway, you give Ted my best."

"But I thought I told you last year Ian," he answered in a harsh voice, "Uncle Ted died. You're getting forgetful in your old age. Don't you remember, it was just after my Auntie Else passed away?"

There were so many bodies in this conversation I was losing track. "Oh yeah of course, yeah, sorry. Anyway…" I started to smile and back away. What with the 'Sally Army' carollers singing Silent Night another few minutes of this depressing conversation and I was going straight home to slash my wrists and as if that wasn't enough he then started on me.

"You look as though you've put on weight since last year," he said with what I thought looked like a smirk. "Your face looks a bit fat too." He laughed as if joking but I had the feeling he was having a dig and silently enjoying it. "All that good living eh Ian?"

I hate that, people saying I've put on weight. In fact

I'd lost it. I wished now I'd ducked his head down the school toilets longer now.

"Just look at the time, I'll miss me last bus," he suddenly announced as if satisfied with his parting shot and suddenly it was him wanting to do a runner. "You always keep me talking Ian. Anyway nice to see you," and added in a low mumble to our lass to rub in the salt, "Make sure he stays off the chocolate over Christmas, he's at that dangerous age." He laughed like it was a joke but I could see he was having another dig.

"Anyway, Merry Christmas Ian and you have a good New Year. Probably see you next year, hopefully." He disappeared into the Christmas crowds, dissolving like a phantom and leaving his last words ominously hanging in the air like a big black cloud.

"What did he mean by that, hopefully? Sarcy bastard!" I said aloud to our lass. Then I silently cursed and for a couple of seconds I stood in the middle of St.Stephen's fuming and looked at our lass.

"I'm not getting fat am I?" I asked her as I inspected myself in a nearby shop window and thought I looked really good, even if I say so myself.

Our lass rolled her eyes. "Yeah you look great Casanova. Now come on will you," and she started to hurry away.

"I should have nutted him," I mumbled to myself.

Memories are strange things, the funny ones you can still laugh at but the bad ones haunt you. I suppose my childhood was no harder than many, it just seemed harder at the time. My mother was a widow and had four kids to look after, three boys and one girl, with me the youngest. My two brothers Colin and Graham were pigeon mad and always around somewhere either stealing pigeons or selling them. And my sister, Yvonne, who was the oldest, spent most of her evenings snogging on the doorstep with a local lad called Allan Cox who was an elder brother of one of my mates Terry Cox. With no man in the house I suppose looking back I was a bit of a tearaway. And down Hessle Road being a tearaway was by no means unique.

There certainly weren't any luxuries and I remember when our next door neighbour down Kate's Terrace, Wassand Street got a television, news went round the street like wild fire and all the kids would spend the evening loitering outside the front window gawping in at the TV. Like all good things it didn't last long though because everything in those days was on the never-never, as credit was called then and it wasn't long before the men came round to take it away because as the name suggests, they never, never paid for it. Something of a fight broke with our neighbour's sons I remember and the TV men who had come to take back the telly got a good pasting for their troubles. They were Fisher Kids (fishermen to the uninitiated) and had just come home from sea and with just three days home and then back to sea again, they had been on the beer all day. And with it being Saturday afternoon they had been watching wrestling with good old "ding, ding, seconds out", Kent Walton at the ringside. Well to coin a dramatic phrase often used in the newspapers, "a scuffle broke out". And what a spectacular scrap it was with no holds barred. All us kids had gathered in a circle egging on the Fisher Kids and jeering the evil TV repo' men. Watching the Fisher Kids scrapping with the TV men beat any wrestling on the TV that day I can tell you. There was blood and snot everywhere and after two falls, two submissions, a forearm smash and a good kick in the balls the TV men beat a hasty retreat back to their Rediffusion van, carrying what was left of a television that had been somewhat wrecked in the fight.

I suppose reading this you might get the impression that Hessle Road was a bit rough and you would be right. With countless trawlers landing every day at St. Andrew's Dock the Fisher Kids had pockets full of money and only three days to booze it away in until the next fishing trip. Oh yes, every night was Saturday night on Hessle Road and what was even better was what money the Fisher Kids didn't spend they would usually drunkenly scramble to the kids waiting outside the pub as they climbed into a taxi taking them back to their ship.

Eventually though even we managed to get a television by way of my Uncle Harold. My gormless Uncle Harold was a bit of a 'ducker and diver' and even though he could not read or write he was a dab hand at fixing tellies, for a few weeks anyway, until they broke down again. Uncle Harold was one of the better known characters on Hessle Road. He was going bald and what was left of his hair he wore long and scruffy down the back of his neck and he never seemed to change his clothes or wash very much. He never stopped telling dirty jokes and talking dirty especially when in the company of women. He also talked so fast it was hard to understand him because added to this he had this terrible hanging stutter that made his words come out like gibberish. You always got the hang of what he was saying eventually though because what he had to say usually started with F and ended with K. Thinking back, I cannot remember ever seeing him without a Park Drive cigarette dog-end hanging from the corner of his mouth and he hardly ever stopped coughing. Most people who knew Uncle Harold took him with a pinch salt because he was just one of many of the real diamond characters of Hessle Road. Nobody was ever quite sure how many kids Uncle Harold had because every time we tried to count them we could never remember all their names but conservative estimates put it at twelve. I remember my Mum saying at his funeral a few years back, "It was a wonder they ever got the coffin lid down."

All I remember about his wife, my Auntie Betty was that she always seemed to be up the duff and had this strange habit of sitting the youngest on her lap with no bottoms on and letting it piss all over the place. The air in that house was so sharp it could take the paint off a stolen bike faster than a blowlamp. So it goes without saying that you avoided the house at all costs save for when the telly broke. Then, me mum would send us round for Uncle Harold's expertise and to give him his due, he always seemed to be able to get it going after a poke with a screw driver here and there once the back was off the TV. I am not sure that he really knew what he was doing and I can remember one night he had been fixing someone's telly down Marmaduke Street and there was an almighty bang from the house. The television came crashing through the front room window and everybody's electric went off including the streetlights. Although Uncle Harold got the blame the locals still used him to fix their televisions after he came out of hospital and he blamed the explosion on a faulty duffer valve in the TV. He made quite a good living I expect fixing all the tellies roundabouts and it was rumoured that it was not always cash that his female customers paid him with. On top of his sick money and mega family allowance my mum grudgingly reckoned he was coining it in and would often comment that his glass back never stopped him propping up the bar in the Criterion Pub every day. You can guess there were lots of jokes about how he got that bad back with his twelve kids and always one in the oven.

CHAPTER TWO

Anyway not to get too bogged down with my Uncle Harold, my story starts in 1955 when I was born at 15 Kate's Terrace, down Wassand Street off Hessle Road. We were called half-caste kids in those days because my Dad had been an Arabic merchant seaman. You can't say half-caste these days because there are so many powerful, posh people who get very offended on our behalf. They are probably the same posh people who wouldn't give us jobs when we left school because we were half-caste with a foreign surname, but I don't want to sound too bitter. It's strange and quite bizarre how times change and later on I changed my surname to my mother's maiden name of Newton, a nice English name so that I could get a job. But now I often find as a contractor, that I can't get a job because I'm English. How's that for bad luck? Funny old world, isn't it? And with all this equality stuff going on these days I often think that I will change my surname back to Achmed but with the luck I have with surnames, you can bet as soon as I changed it back the BNP will get elected.

Anyway, there were a few of us half-castes knocking about up and down Hessle Road in those days because Hull was a merchant shipping port as well as a fishing port. And I often heard my mum say that the Arabs used to "put it about a lot" when their ships came in. My Dad popped his clogs a couple of months before I was born and ended up being buried in Cuba or so the story goes, so he won't feature much in my story because I didn't get to know him that well you understand. I did ask my mum why they didn't bring him home to be buried in Hull and will never forget her reply. She said that the deep freeze on the ship had broken down and by the time they would have got him back to Hull he would have stank the ship out, so they planted him in Cuba instead. I always was an inquisitive child.

Our first house on Hessle Road was in Wassand Street and was a two-up-two-down with an outside tap and toilet and four of us slept in one back bedroom. Our back yard backed onto Skinners Taxi's Garage and across the terrace was a patch of waste land where a couple of houses had once stood before being bombed out by the Germans Fokkers, read that as you please. In those days there were lots of areas in streets on Hessle Road with spaces like that. We would play football on them or on bonfire night we would pile all the wood we had collected or pinched off other streets like Walcott Street and have a street party and dance around the bonfire like little Red Indians and throw bricks and bangers over the wall at the Walcott Street gang who were having their bonfire on the other side of the wall. Oh yes, happy days unless you were on the receiving end of a brick being thrown back. I did get caught a few times and kept the scars to show for it for quite a while. But I console myself with the knowledge that there were more on the receiving end of the bricks I threw than ever landed on my bonce. The end of our street backed on to some railway lines and there was a bridge we kids used to call Stricky Bridge, after Strickland Street. There was a big set of steps going up to the bridge and then the bridge itself took you across the railway lines before breaking off in two directions. One long stairway would take you down to what we called 'long lane' behind the steam engine sheds and warehouses, which ran parallel with all the docks and eventually led into town. On a night the lane was a really spooky place with lots of secluded places that were overgrown, which you could hide in. On many a summer's night we used to play hide and seek down there and sometimes as we explored the lane we found all sorts of little holes in walls and ways into the warehouses. The places would be stacked with wooden crates and it wasn't long before we were regularly in the warehouses routing about and breaking open crates to see if there were any goodies inside. But usually the crates were filled with machines or machine parts that we didn't understand. Sometimes though, we found useful stuff like reels of lead or copper and we would cut some of it off the drums and sell it to the local rag man. In those days you used to see lots of people sneaking down the lane on a night to steal coal from the engine sheds and there was always lots of old wooden train sleepers that people would also steal to cut up to burn. The other way over the bridge led onto another big green iron bridge that led onto the docks. It had gates that were always locked and sometimes we used to climb over but at the other end of the bridge the stairs that went down onto the docks were guarded by a police box, manned day and night by a copper and if he caught you on the docks you always got sent to juvenile court for trespassing. We often sneaked passed the copper onto the docks and would go exploring the ships moored around the dock and often the foreign seaman would let us on board, show us round and give us tea and something to eat in the galley and tell us exciting stories about where they were from and where they were sailing to next. It was stories and experiences like these that gave many of us ambitions to go sea.

After school lots of us used to charge down to Stricky Bridge before going home and sit on the bridge as a number of steam engines would pass under it at that time of day and we would all disappear in the steam blowing out from the engines. In winter Stricky Bridge would become a magnet for all the kids on Hessle Road because when the snow fell and the steps of the bridge froze we'd slide down them on big pieces of hardboard. Sometimes four and five of us would squeeze onto the hardboard and launch ourselves from the top and we'd travel down that stairway at the speed of an Olympic bobsleigher. It was exciting and good fun on the way down but as you can imagine once we hit the bottom the hardboard would come to a sudden crashing halt and we would all be thrown off it and be sent rolling onto the pavement. At one time or another we all got our share of bumps and grazes and others got hurt badly with broken legs, arms and cracked skulls but it never seemed to stop us. There were no playgrounds on Hessle Road and so our playgrounds were whatever was around us and usually forbidden to us. I suppose that is what made our adventures that bit more exciting and that sometimes we would get caught in the wrong place at the wrong time. If it was just something minor like being on Stricky Bridge we would get reported to school usually by the Transport Police and for that reason me and my friends Frankie Callis and Johnny Butler were always being caned or getting a good bollocking off the headmistress at Daltry Street School.

I suppose it was for this reason I was reminded many times as a child, especially by the head mistress at Daltry Street infants, Miss Swift that Wassand Street was the scruffiest street in Hull and I would end up in Borstal if I didn't mend my ways. We had got off on the wrong foot a few years earlier during my first year in infants when she got very upset after several in our class including myself, Frankie Callis and Tony Brewer had had a pissing competition to see who could piss out of the playground toilet window. Although I won, very easily I might add, the fountain coming out of the toilet window was spotted and traced back to me and I was foisted off to Miss Swift's office in the middle of my victory dance by Mrs Taylor who was on playground duty and had eye-balled me as the winning culprit. Miss Swift screamed at me until she was almost blue in the face and gave me a massive clout across the lug-hole and stood me in the corridor until dinner time.

After that I had the feeling she had it in for me but I never pissed out of the school toilet window again, at play time that is. Miss Swift was an odious looking old woman with great red curls in her hair that she used to wear up in a big bun and her face was absolutely white with thick pancake makeup and great lips smothered to death in bright red lipstick. She was always puffing endlessly on Embassy filter cigarettes every time I had cause to be in her office. She always reminded me of Miss Faversham in the film Great Expectations and all that was missing out of her office was the crusty old wedding cake that was in the film.

My Mum always said what Miss Swift needed was a man to give her "a good seeing to". I always wondered what she meant but it would only be a few months until I would discover partly what Mum meant. One day after school one of my mates Colin Pennycad said one of the girls in our class had taken him into a bombed house, pulled her knickers down and showed him her 'bits' and he'd only had to give her two penny toffee dainties in the way of payment. Colin Pennycad always did know a good deal when he saw one. It would be wrong to name names here but anyone reading this that was in our class from 1960 until 1965 at Daltry Street infants and juniors will know the girl who I am talking about but just to prick your memory her initials were L.O. Colin Pennycad told me there was to be a second showing that night and asked did I want to come. Why not I thought, after all it was still something of a mystery to me at six years old why girls wore tight black knickers during dance class and nothing stuck out. After a run on penny toffee dainties at the local sweet shop down Daltry Street word seemed to have got around our class and after school all the boys piled into this dark and dingy bombed house down Strickland Street. It was a good job Colin Pennycad brought his Dad's torch because I couldn't see anything. Always practical like that Colin Pennycad, I think he took his talents with a torch into his professional life and became a night watchman after he left school. Anyway the girl did her stuff and Colin shone the torch on her and we were all giggling like daft schoolboys, of course being daft schoolboys. It was just like Sunday Night at The London Palladium with this girl showing everything under the spotlight of Colin Pennycad's torch. Even in those days I suppose everybody wanted to be famous and I suppose our little secret get-together in that derelict house might have been the first ever 'X-factor' audition in another time but it was definitely a "No" from me. I remember afterwards the whole experience left me a bit confused because the girl didn't have one, if you know what I mean and it was all a bit of an anti-climax and I almost asked for my penny toffee dainties back.

Anyway, I gave the matter no further thought and could not understand why Colin had made such a fuss over literally nothing. I went to school the next day my happy little whistling self but there waiting for me in the classroom with a face like my Granny's arse was Miss Swift. You are not going to believe this but somehow Miss Swift had found out about our extra curricular activities and I had been fingered for it. I was dragged physically out of the class by my hair with Miss Swift screaming like a banshee, what a dirty, disgusting little tyke I was to all the class and I was given six of the best with a slipper in front of the whole school at assembly the next morning. Miss Swift never even mentioned the name Colin Pennycad and I could not help but feel that I had been set up by Colin as the patsy. Miss Swift even told my Mum who gave me another pasting, sent me up to bed and banned me from watching Thunderbirds for a month. To this day I blame my headmistress Miss Swift for that. Can you believe it, a whole month with no Thunderbirds? Generally I got the impression that Miss Swift did not like me very much but I did get my own back on her. Her car seemed to be off the road for weeks after about four of us pissed in her petrol tank and I felt sure that any call to International Rescue would fall on deaf ears... F.A.B. Scott.

When I was seven years old we got a little bit posher and moved across Hessle Road into Marmaduke Street, which was then known as the second scruffiest street in Hull but soon became the first after they pulled down Wassand Street. So our rise up the social ladder, so to speak did not last that long but at least we had three bedrooms, an attic and the back room could take a bigger tin bath.

Although I had had some good times down Wassand Street and had some good friends everybody seemed to move away to the new posh estates being built like Preston Road – well it was posh in those days, as was Orchard Park and the mega posh Bilton Grange. My Mum said they had hot water, real baths and electric lights bulbs on those estates not like our gas mantle lamps. Anyway it still made no difference to us because none of us wanted to move off Hessle Road. In fact we were one of the last families to move out of Wassand Street and all us kids that were left had a whale of a time helping pull down or setting fire to the condemned houses. We would often rake through a house recently vacated because they always left loads of stuff like old couches and settees and we would pull them to bits, looking for the money that had slipped down the sides. In one house we found fifty full green shield stamp books left by some old biddy and we got half a crown a book when we took them to the local shop. We were all well coined that night and we all waited outside Bev's off -licence down Constable Street asking those going in to get us ten number six ciggies, a box of matches and a cheap bottle of plonk. We all got bombed out of our heads and ended up in Gordon Street Police Station waiting for our parents and I got another one of my usual pastings but I do remember that my mum kept the fags for herself.

When I think back to some of the antics we got up to I cringe and wonder how did any of us ever make it out alive? One of the stunts we use to pull was to pile old mattresses into a back yard of a condemned house, climb up on the roof and shout to the people shopping on Hessle Road and then jump off the roof. All the people would scream thinking we had fallen but of course we landed on the mattresses. I did have one really close shave and I was lucky not to be killed. One day after school me and my mate Frankie Callis decided to pull the jumping off the roof stunt in some part-demolished house down Strickland Street. We had been doing it the day before to great effect for the happy shoppers on Hessle Road. Anyway the demolition men had boarded up the house but we managed to squeeze through a hole in the back door. During the day the demolition men had taken out the floors but the stairs were still intact so we went up to the bedroom level and climbed into the false roof. The roof had also gone so we had a full view of Hessle Road. We started shouting our usual 'regale' at the shoppers on Hessle Road and just as usual they stood awe-struck in horror watching me and Frankie doing our tribal dance on what was left of the roof walls. Having seen Hop Along Cassidy at the Langham Cinema shoot a baddy the previous Saturday I was determined to emulate the baddy's fall off the wall and Frankie obliged by a pretend shot in the guts from a piece of piping that he used as a make believe gun. Anyway my fall was just beautiful. As Frank shot me I clutched my belly to dramatic effect and slowly keeled over and almost in slow motion dived off the roof. I could hear the usual screams from those watching from Hessle Road and chuckled to myself on the way down - but not for long. All I remembered next was waking up in hospital with a copper by my bedside and my Mum crying and going on about my dirty underpants. Apparently the demolition men had moved the mattresses in the afternoon and being young and totally daft I had not checked. I mean, you don't do you when you're seven, check no one's moved the mattresses I mean. Anyway the copper told me I was lucky to be alive and had missed hitting a solid fireplace by inches, as if crashing onto a pile of bricks was some consolation. I came out of it relatively unscathed with just a small inch size hole in my side that the hospital nurse stitched up. If I learned my lesson it didn't last long and me and me mates were back in the derelict houses a few weeks later scavenging, making dens and generally doing really evil but funny stuff that kids like to do.

Well eventually the time came to move across the road into Marmaduke Street. I had watched no end of vans and lorries moving people and thought nothing of it. I was also looking forward to the ride in the lorry even though it was just across the road. It never entered my head that the physical act of moving would cause me so much embarrassment. My mother always had to be different and because my Dad was "brown bread" my mum never had any money, not that anyone else did either on Hessle Road. They used to say about Hessle Road that you could leave your door open and no one would take anything. And that was perfectly true mainly because no one had anything worth nicking. Anyway not to get distracted, why should moving house cause a seven-year-old boy such embarrassment I hear you say? As I said when you move a lorry or a van takes your stuff, I mean you would never think anything else would you. I remember running home from school all excited knowing we was moving and I stopped dead in my tracks at the top of our terrace. There was my half-wit Uncle Harold with his half-wit mate loading all our worldly belongings onto the local ragman's horse and cart. Yes, you got it, a horse and cart. Oh the shame and embarrassment. All the local kids were out dancing around the horse and cart sounding off at the top of their voices the Steptoe theme tune. Even my own girl friend at the time Susan Fletcher was laughing and generally taking the piss. I really thought I meant more to her than that and thought we were getting serious after a hot session of kiss cats only that very afternoon at play time in the girls' toilets. Women can be so hurtful and I blew her out after that and deliberately took up with her arch rival at school the lovely Linda Lutkin and would deliberately give her a big smacking kiss with some gusto whenever Susan Fletcher crossed our path. Vengeance is so sweet.

CHAPTER THREE

You might think because we had lived just across Hessle Road in Wassand Street that it would have been no big deal moving to Marmaduke Street as we were bound to know some of the people that lived there. Hessle Road was not like that though. You lived down your own street and as children you tended to keep to your own street and even to your own side of the road. It was very territorial in those days and it might seem strange that even though I had lived just across the road I had never been down Marmaduke Street. Even the kids down Marmaduke Street went to a different school called Constable Street. The kids on my side of Hessle Road went to Daltry Street School. So when we moved none of us knew anybody who lived down Marmaduke Street apart from the few like us from Wassand Street and that side of Hessle Road who had chosen to move into Marmaduke Street. The mates from my side of the road and the same school who also moved down Marmaduke Street were, the Butler family, the Callis family and the Manstons and Whitakers.

My family was something of a novelty since we were the only half-caste family in the area although there was also another half-caste, black family in the next street called the Harts. Later we got to be good friends as many of us would in Marmaduke Street in the months and years to come but sometimes we did get a hard time because of our colour. But with our family it was a case of, "what doesn't kill you makes you stronger" and with all the other weird characters living down Marmaduke Street having brown skin was low on the weirdo scale. One thing about Marmaduke Street that stuck out was that all the houses were painted green and because they were council owned you could not paint them any other colour. Wassand Street had been private landlords and so you could have your house any colour. I just thought I would throw that in as a point of interest for any architectural historical types who might read this book.

I suppose having talked so much about some of the unique characters that lived in and around Marmaduke Street I should take you on a little tour of the street and introduce you to some of them and also to some of the kids that would become my friends.

To start with my Uncle Harold lived about ten doors down the street from my house, on the same side of the road. For a few months we managed to keep it quiet that we were related but it did eventually get out and it was more to my Uncle Harold's embarrassment that he was related to half-castes than us being related to the local scruffs. Later we discovered that it had been Uncle Harold more than us who had been trying to keep it quiet that we were related. Oh well, some you lose I suppose. Next door to my Uncle Harold on his left was the Appleby family who were relatively normal although rumour had it Mr Appleby worked, which seemed to be born out by the fact that his son Barry had a new racing bike that wasn't stolen. Whilst Barry would not let anyone lend it he would always give some of us cross bar rides down the street before we graduated onto to stealing our own. On Uncle Harold's right hand side lived Joe Johnson or as he was more endearingly known to the kids in the streets as Stuttering Joe Johnson. He was a real misery guts and if you were playing football outside his house he would come out to clear you off but it was generally time to go in by the time he got all his words out. It was always a mystery to me as a kid why he bothered moving us on since most of his windows had already been broken and boarded up anyway by kids playing football. Uncle Harold and stuttering Joe hated each other's guts and some of us kids would often wind up my Uncle Harold about stuff we would say Joe had said about him. We would be real subtle and say stuff like, Joe had said he was a mucky bastard and his house stunk. It was so funny watching Joe and my Uncle Harold having a toe-to-toe slanging match in the street because they both stuttered. They would dance around like two old fashioned boxers, fists in the air.

"I'm gonna f,f,f,f,fucking kill ya!" My Uncle Harold would shout.

"Go on Harold, you tell him." We'd all shout, "Stick one on him Harold!"

"You just, f,f,f,f,fucking try it." Joe would shout back.

By the time they had finished arguing and prancing about they had actually never started, no one had laid a punch on the other and they could never get to the bottom of why they had started arguing in the first place. Just around the corner from Joe's house was Hilda's Terrace and Mr and Mrs Fox lived down there. They had a son called Michael that you never saw except for school holidays when they let him home from Borstal. I make no exaggeration when I say Michael was the worst thief in the world. He never ever finished one of his holidays from Borstal before he was getting lifted by the police for stealing or breaking in somewhere and got carted off early back to borstal. He was so unlucky it was unbelievable. One night he joined in with some local kids who were throwing bricks at the streetlights but he missed and hit the windscreen of a police car turning into the street. And then instead of running away down the street like all the other kids, Mike made a real clever get-away running in full view into his house. Mike's Dad, Old Man Foxy was another pearl of Marmaduke Street. All us kids liked to call him Foxy because he actually looked just like his name. He was lean like a racing snake with sharp poker features and a long foxy nose and was always smiling to himself like he was a nut case. He was always trying to flog something that he had got cheap from Melville's sale rooms down Coltman Street. Everywhere he went he pushed this rusty old pram, usually with a broken television on it and he would always give you a furtive nod and wink and ask in a whisper, "Don't know anybody who wants a telly do you?" or "You haven't got a spare cig on you?" And he would mince off down the street pushing his pram with a telly on it with this big mental grin on his face. Foxy always had some scheme on the go for making a bob or two, only his schemes always seemed to go tits up big style and us kids would usually be the main reason. I remember I was about twenty-two and living in a flat down Anlaby Road in Hull. I was walking along Anlaby Road with a bird on my way to my flat with plans of having my wicked way with her, when, minding my own business this voice shouted after me. I turned and it was old man Foxy and he was pushing a pram with a telly on it purposely towards me with a big smile of greeting on his face at seeing an old acquaintance from Marmaduke Street. I couldn't believe it and after all those years and he was still pushing that pram and the first words he said to me was, "You don't know anyone who wants a telly? Have you got a cig on you?" Since I was with this bird I just pretended not to know him, quickly put my collar up and walked on.

Across the street from my Uncle Harold was old Jimmy. God only knows how old Jimmy was. He looked over a hundred but was little, lean and mean and bounced around on the balls of his feet wearing these hob-nail boots like a featherweight boxer. If anybody remembers Billy Whiz the comic strip character he looked just like him and could move just as fast when you knocked on his door and ran away. He would be opening his front door before you had finished knocking and would chase you down the street at full pelt mumbling incoherently and frothing at the mouth. If he caught you he would knock ten bells of shit out of you and if your Dad or big brother went round complaining he would give them a good kicking too. It was like an initiation ceremony for new kids to the street to get them to play "Knock off Ginger" on Jimmy's door and run.

"Go on," we'd say, "he's only an old man."

They'd knock, and zoom, Jimmy would be out the door like a whippet after a hare. There were few he did not catch and that was what made it so much fun and I think maybe in his own way Jimmy enjoyed it too, especially pasting us kids when he caught us.

My old friend from Daltry Street school Johnny Butler had moved in just up the street from us on the corner of the first terrace coming in from Hessle Road. Backing onto the Butler's house down the terrace lived Taffy Touchwood. He would go down the street kissing the floor and touching all the wooden doors and telephone poles. If you could get him in conversation he would talk for hours about all the women he had known and would give you all the real mucky details about what he got up to with them. We would often go into his house and he would let us read all his dirty books. It was unusual for us to wind him up because he had this very unsociable habit of posting dog shit through your door to get his own back. Your mum always knew if you had been teasing him because there was always dog shit in your hallway the next morning and you would get a pasting for your troubles. Although there were many other characters down Marmaduke Street, just for the moment I have described some of the main stay characters, we as kids down Marmaduke Street had so much fun with and the others I will draw in as my story unfolds.

One of my best mates was Frankie Callis, he was dark skinned like me and always told me he was half gypsy but he still got lumbered with being called a half-caste. In our little rabble, that you might call a gang but not in the gangster sense, were my other mates including Terry Cox, Johnny Butler and Joey Manston. Later on, as we all moved on into Boulevard Senior School, Jimmy Turner joined us. We nicknamed Jimmy Turner, Isse after the Hessle Road pawnbroker, Isador Turner who we used to take all our nicked stuff to and pawn. Isse was from Beecroft Street, sort of on Hessle Road and sort of not but he fitted in really well with us and like the rest of us loved mischief and fun. Isse's house backed onto Division Road cemetery. It was full of really old graves and very overgrown with high grass and no one ever tidied it up. There were lots of places to hide and it was one of the places we would often go to have some midnight fun because it was also a very, very spooky place. Today they have turned it into a park and I have no idea what happened to the bodies. In those days it was also very handy for the fisher kids leaving Rayners pub on the corner of West Dock Avenue if they had a girl in toe because it was just across the road from the pub. There was many a night we watched from behind a gravestone as some drunken couple had a mad passionate sexual ding-dong in the middle of the cemetery. We would often take our catapults and peashooters into the graveyard and hide out waiting for some unsuspecting couple. Terry Cox had this giant torch and we would sit silently listening and laughing under our breath until the couple got into their stride and were hammering away at each other on a grave slab. It was then ambush time and we would suddenly turn on the torch often catching some fisher kid's shiny arse in the powerful beam doing vigorous press ups and all fire our catapults and peashooters at once in one big broadside at his arse. Then we'd shout something like, "Stop shagging ya dirty bastards!" and run like hell.

Screams and blue language would echo round the graveyard.

"I'll fucking kill you kids when I get my hands on

ya.!" But by the time the fisher kid had got his trousers back on we had retreated to the safety of Isse Turner's back yard laughing our little socks off. Sometimes we would get chased around the graveyard and if they would have caught us they would have given us a real good hiding for interrupting their night of passion but they never did. We were not that daft and if they did chase us we had already prepared a path to run through that we had laid with booby traps like covered holes and trip wires. One night Isse, me, Frankie and Terry Cox dug this great big hole about six feet deep in the graveyard. Sometimes gypsies used to tether their horses on a corner of the graveyard so there was always lots of horse shit around the place. This night we borrowed Isse's Dad's garden barrow and filled it with horse shit and tipped it in to our hole. We then covered the hole up with cardboard and covered it with grass. We had dug the hole just near the place that was popular with 'midnight shaggers'. It looked really natural in the dark and you would have never known that there was a great big hole full of horse shit underneath. The hole was situated in such a place that it would be directly in the path of anyone who was chasing us. We only had to wait an hour or so and we spotted this fisher kid coming into the graveyard with a bird. You could tell it was a fisher kid out on the beer for his three-day binge because they had their hair greased back like a poor man's Elvis Presley. And they always wore one of them two piece suits with big baggy trousers and a jacket with a belt and two pleats on the back. And they would usually be drunk. They got down to business really quickly and we started making hooting noises like an owl.

We could hear the girl whispering, "What's that?" We then started making noises like a ghost. "Whoooo! Whooooo!" We had this big tin and if you said something into it, it would echo. Isse started talking into it and it sounded really spooky. The girl was now on her feet pulling up her drawers.

"I tell you there's something out there," she said but the fisher kid was trying to pull her back down onto the grass.

"It's just kids mucking about," he shouted. "If I get my hands on ya I'll break ya neck!"

We then came out from behind a gravestone and started shouting and waving at him in the dark.

"Come and get us then!"

"It's little kids," squawked the girl angrily, "little bastards."

"I'll have ya," shouted the fisher kid and he was on his feet and running towards us but not for long and he fell into our hole with a big scream. We rushed forward and threw some buckets of horse shit into the hole on top of him.

"I'll fucking kill ya," shouted the fisher kid. By this time the girl came running over screaming at us and in the dark she did not see the hole either and she fell in too. I could not repeat what the two of them were screaming and shouting at us because as a little kid I was taught not to use such language but the gist was a lot of swearing with descriptions of what they would do when they got their hands on us. We ran off like the wind, laughing so much that we could hardly get our breath…

Another night the four us were hiding out with the lights off and having a little party of our own in Isse's back bedroom that looked out on the cemetery. Isse's Mum and Dad had gone to the pub and we were house sitting with him. We would have been about twelve or thirteen at the time. Anyway, Isse's brother had just come home from sea and we had pinched some of his cigs and beer out of his kit bag and were all 'well gone' and in full mischief mode. There was me, Terry Cox, Frankie Callis and Isse and we were watching the cemetery with a pair of binoculars on the hunt for midnight shaggers when about three fisher kids came into the graveyard with a girl each in tow and no doubt planning a night of passion. They were all absolutely pissed out of their heads and had also brought some beer and other drink with them.

"Look at this," said Isse, starting to laugh as he looked through the binoculars. By now we were all fighting for a look.

They were having a right old orgy and general booze up right in the middle of the cemetery and there were trousers and knickers flying in all directions. We were all looking at each other and laughing.

"Let's get 'em," said Terry. We crept downstairs and out the back of the house and into the cemetery and slowly crawled behind some gravestones only a few yards from where they were. We could see some of their clothes piled in a heap but they were all too busy with each other to notice us.

"Let's nick the clothes," I said in a whisper and we snuck up commando style, grabbed a pile of clothes and ran back to Isse's back yard. I noticed in the back yard Isse's outside tap was connected to a long hosepipe and so we reeled out the hosepipe and quietly snuck back through the long grass. We were about ten feet away when we let them have it. We pretended to shout like grown ups as we gave them a good soaking from the hosepipe.

"Go on ya dirty little bastards. I know who you girls are and I'll be telling ya mothers in the morning." The girls were screaming and were up and running faster than a whippet and they didn't even stop to look for their knickers. We could hear the drunken fisher kids scrambling about looking for their trousers.

"The Police are here now!" Isse shouted in a grown up voice and they too were up and running, tripping and falling over gravestones with their bare arses shining in the moonlight. We ran back to Isse's back yard, our sides aching with laugher.

Some nights we would dress up in old peoples' clothes. I would wear Isse's Dad's working coat, put on a flat cap, a muffler scarf and his Dad's glasses and Isse would put on of his mother's pinny and overcoat on and wear a woman's 'turban' on his head. He looked more like Old Mother Riley and we would walk through the graveyard arm in arm like an old married couple shouting our outrage at the couples rolling about in the grass. "Why ya dirty little buggers," we'd shout and they would run full pelt out the graveyard.

CHAPTER FOUR

I suppose that because our parents hadn't much money to speak of, it naturally meant that they had none to give to us kids. So we made our own fun and found our own ways of earning our own money, more often than not it was by hook or by crook and mainly by crook. Sometimes we did get the odd few pennies to go swimming at Madeley Street baths and it didn't matter if you had no swimming trunks and we didn't, they would let you go swimming in the bear buff as we called it. The two-penny swimming baths at Madeley Street would always be full and kids from all over Hessle Road who would not only use them for a good swim but it would save their mums from having to get the tin bath out the back yard once a week. Unfortunately the baths were only open in summer and in winter the baths would be boarded out and would be used for roller skating and Wrestling - and that's another story. Madeley Street baths would chuck out at about three o'clock and we would always emerge into the afternoon sunshine with our eyes sore and all our skins all crinkled up because we had been swimming in the heavily chlorinated water for hours. Everybody pissed in the water and you would also get a turd regularly floating about in the water. The attendant would have to fish it out with a small net on a long pole but having a big brown "submarine" chasing you around the pool was usually a good way of quickly emptying the baths. We always came out absolutely starving and some kids would make a beeline for Goodfellows store just across the road to get three-penny worth of broken biscuits and for that price you would get a massive bag. Our gang usually never had any money in those early days so first we would go round the back of the Liberal Club just at the top of Coltman Street and climb over the back wall. They used to store all their empty bottles in the yard and we would nick half a crate full of beer bottles and then go round to the front and take them in and get three pennies a bottle. It worked like a charm every week and we would then go back to Goodfellows and get a big bag of broken biscuits each. It took them years to twig on we were stealing their bottles and taking them back for the deposit.

When I think back, I am quite amazed at the number of scams we had as children. We were always at the pictures but we never paid. We would sneak in using several different ways to fool the cinema ushers that we had evolved to almost perfection. In Hull in those days there were loads of cinemas because having a television was a luxury most could not afford and there were only two TV channels anyway.

There was ABC cinema near the bus station, Saturday morning was ABC minors when under tens and also lots of over tens would pile in for Batman and Robin, Hopalong Cassidy and some crap feature film. Most of the time you would just go for a snog on the back row and sometimes you would get more adventurous things going on in the back row with the bigger boys and girls, it was sometimes better watching them than the film. The ushers would come round shining their torches.

"You can stop that you dirty little buggers," they would shout and throw you out if they caught you feeling a girl's tits. I suppose we got most of our sex education in that way but I have to admit even during my 'ABC Minor days' how babies were made was still somewhat of a mystery to most of us. I remember a big boy did tell me once and he claimed he had done it with a girl but I just didn't believe him. I guessed he was winding me up because he could not answer my further questioning on what it was like and it also sounded horrible. If that's what you had to do to have sex you could count me out I thought, but not for too long I hasten to add. In those days there was a scale of numbers for what you could get off a girl and every kid on Hessle Road knew what the scale meant. Twenty-five was a kiss, fifty was a feel of her tits, seventy-five, also known as the smelly finger and one hundred and the rest I am sure I can leave to your imagination, so I won't go on. Suffice to say you generally graduated onto the seventy-five and one hundred scale when you got into your teens. Our little mob never really went much to ABC Minors, we would go around town during week days on a night to see the X rated films, sneak in and keep our heads down when the usher came round. Cecil cinema was another regular haunt we used to sneak into, it is still there today but used for bingo I think. Cecil was always an easy one to sneak into and the good thing about Cecil was that if you sneaked in whilst the picture was on the staff always left the ice cream and sweet counter unattended. We would just help ourselves, wait till somebody went to the toilet and then go into the main cinema fully 'goodied up' as they were coming out. I must have seen 'The Sound of Music' a hundred times because they ran it for almost six months once and 'Gone With The Wind' seemed to be on for months as well. "Frankly my dear I don't give a damn," doesn't sound as catchy when you've heard it twenty or thirty times and I would have asked for my money back if I'd have paid.

Down George Street there was the Dorchester and we saw all the Carry On Films there and we loved them. Our favourite was 'Carry On Screaming' but it also gave us loads of ideas for having some fun. Anyone who has seen 'Carry On Screaming' will remember a Frankenstein-like monster in the film called Odvod. He was massive with big broad shoulders and had a Werewolf haircut with big sharp teeth to match and he wore this blue boiler suit. A

46

Frankenstein werewolf in a blue boiler suite could only happen in a Carry On film. In the film Odvod was kidnapping all the women out courting on the common at night and would take them back to this old Mansion. We were all really taken with Odvod and one night were all at Isse's house playing with his Ouija board and were scaring each other to death. We were always playing on Isse's Ouija board and we would all sit around his living room table in the dark with our fingers on the pointer trying to contact the dead and scaring each other to death. What always fascinated me about Ouija boards is that they seemed to work and whilst we all suspected each other of pushing the pointer it was still real scary. We had hit on the idea that ghosts might be able to tell the future and so that night we tried to contact a spirit that might be able to give us some winning horses so we could put a bet on them. Isse had got a daily paper so we could put some horse names to the board and we all put our fingers on the board and asked if there was anybody there. Like a shot the pointer started dragging around the board. "You're pushing it Isse!" I shouted at him half-scared.

"I'm not, honest. It's Frankie!"

"It's not me, honest!" Frankie protested in a scared voice. "Look it's spelling something!"

The pointer sped across the board, first to A, then D, then O, then L, then F.

"What's that spell?" I asked loudly.

"Fucking hell," Terry answered, "Adolf!" Then the pointer started moving again, H, then I, then T, then L, then E, then R, and then it suddenly stopped moving.

"It's Adolf Hitler," said Isse.

We all started laughing, "It's you pushing it Isse," I said again.

"It's not, honest. Let's ask him."

As daft as it seems Isse read out the names of horses riding in a race on Saturday. One by one as Isse named the horses, the pointer slid in and out of "No" until he came to a horse called Millbank, "Is Millbank going to win tomorrow?" Isse asked in a spooky voice and then the pointer sped into "Yes".

"That's it," said Isse all excited. "It's Millbank!"

We played on and Hitler gave us the names of five more winners running on the next day which was Saturday. Eventually Hitler got pissed off with talking to us because like all kids that play on Ouija boards we started asking daft questions like, "What was it like in Hell? And was it hot?" and he put the phone down so to speak, as anybody would after getting verbally abused and Hitler had more than his fair share of problems on his plate already without having four piss taking kids ringing him up on an Ouija board.

Playing with an Ouija board can be scary at the best of times but when you have a cemetery on your back door it sort of focuses your attention. One of Isse's neighbours was a nosey old woman who lived alone and was always telling Isse's mum and dad that we were causing trouble and making a noise. She had been banging on the wall all night because we had been shouting and laughing as we played with the Ouija board. Isse disappeared upstairs and came back down with his hair back combed and had his brothers blue boiler suite on with the shoulders all padded out. We were in stitches, the boiler suite was way too big but the hair and shoulders were just right and apart from being too small he looked just like the monster Odvod from Carry On Screaming. At about ten O'clock the old women came knocking on Isse's door and started shouting that she would call the Police about the noise. I answered the door and said we would keep the noise down. We decided to modify Isse's Odvod clothing and exchanged the boiler suite for his big brother's long donkey jacket, padded out the shoulders and Isse got on my shoulders. We turned the light out and our silhouette in the dark looked just Odvod the monster from the film with big massive shoulders and a square head. We decided to test our Odvod monster out in the Cemetery. It was pitch dark outside and I just walked through the cemetery with Isse on my shoulders. Several people walking through the cemetery screamed and ran for their lives. Outside the cemetery a great crowd of people had gathered and we heard one woman crying hysterically and screaming, "It was horrible, about seven feet tall!" They were all looking in the cemetery and a few minutes later a police car pulled up outside the cemetery and two coppers came in with torches shining and we scarpered quickly back into Isse's house. We were not finished yet with Odvod the monster and took him out into Beecroft Streeet. The old woman's house had a glass front door and we had a street lamp at our backs and we guessed the old woman would get a real scare at the monster silhouette knocking on her door. So we knocked on her door dressed up as Odvod and all this old woman saw was this seven-foot silhouette with massive shoulders and a square head standing outside her door. "Who's that?" she shouted through the frosted glass. Isse growled just like Ovod the monster in the film Carry On Screaming and the old woman screamed blue murder and we all ran in. Funnily enough the old woman never bothered us again. The next morning we all met up excited outside the betting shop on the corner of Cholmley Street and had decided to go for broke and put a pound on the nose on each of the horses Hitler had given us the night before. All miserable sods going in refused to put a bet on for us and we were almost resigned to failure when Frankie's big brother came up the street to put a bet on him self and he put all the bets on for us. Well satisfied, all we had to do now was sit back and count the coin. We raced over to Isse's house to watch the first race and sat there all excited for the first race and suddenly they were off.

"Come on Millbank!" we all shouted at the telly,

"Come on Millbank!" Isse's mother gave us all curious looks as we screamed at the telly and Millbank sailed home leaving the rest of the field almost standing. We couldn't believe it Hitler had come through for us. Unfortunately his tips were not so hot on the other four races, two fell, one jockey fell off and in the final race our horse came last. "Well at least we got one winner," I said aloud and we went to collect our winnings. Being kids none of us understood odds and the man who went in to collect our winnings came out and plonked two quid in our hands. Millbank was the evens favourite so we came out three quid down on the day. The moral of the story is, that if you ever contact Adolf Hitler on an Ouija Board don't ask him anything about racing because he's a lousy tipster.

Another cinema just up the road from the Dorchester was The Criterion and it had two big gold lions, one on each side of the main entrance. That was one of the easiest to sneak into and we always sneaked in the front way because the ticket office was quite high and as people would go in and pay, we would bob down behind them and go under the ticket desk. The people would just laugh at our cheek and never spragged us up for sneaking in. If you wanted to see a real dirty groin throbbing film then you would go to Tower or Regent. Regent especially was where all the dirty old men would go to watch the really blue films. We would go down the alley at the side, climb onto the toilet roof where there was a sky light and climb through and just go through one door and be in the balcony section. One night Terry, Isse, Frankie and me all sneaked in and a real dirty film was on called 'I A Woman'.

I was never quite sure what the title meant and it was in subtitles but you did not need subtitles to understand what was going on. In fact you did not need any dialogue. It was about this decrepit old man who was dying in hospital and all he seemed to do was put his hand up the skirt of some gorgeous Swedish nurse. The next thing you knew she was getting all worked up, as we all were, then stripping off and climbing into bed with the old man. Lucky old sod - you never got treatment like that at Hull Royal Infirmary - but that was the plot in a nutshell.

In the peasant seats downstairs 'the black mac' brigade' was in en mass and sometimes it was more entertaining watching them. As the mucky bits in the film got all hot and steamy you could see some of them were giving it loads under their coats on the old hand pump and of course we couldn't resist shooting at them with peashooters from the balcony. I know what you are thinking, it's a bad business when you can't even go to the cinema and have a quiet wank in peace but we were only kids. One night we had all sneaked in Regent and downstairs the place was full of 'the black mac' brigade'. This bloke next to us was so amused to see four young kids sat watching he bought us all an ice cream and an orange juice. We sat there all night flicking ice cream at the dirty old men downstairs from the balcony. In those days you could buy orange juice in like pyramid shaped cardboard containers. Of course we got carried away as usual and Isse tore the top of this container of orange juice and lobbed the lot at this old bloke in a circle seat downstairs who was eagerly pulling the head off it under his coat downstairs. It crashed with a big splash right on this old bloke's head. For some reason this bloke downstairs blamed this courting couple behind him for throwing the orange juice and he climbed over his seat, smacked this bloke a real cracker on the nose and they started fighting. And before you knew it everybody downstairs was fighting and we were throwing everything down off the balcony, ice cream, orange juice, ice lollies, the lot went over the balcony. Soon the lights came on, the picture was stopped and the police came swarming in and laid into those fighting downstairs. Everybody upstairs was laughing their heads off. Watching what was going on downstairs was better than the picture.

Isse popped his little head over the balcony and shouted like an outraged grown up. "Do you lot mind down there. We paid good money to see this picture."

There were also lots of other opportunities in those days around town. Every night Hull town centre was like a bright adventure playground with lots of shops and pubs with people milling about. It wasn't just Hessle Road that was busy with Fisher Kids drinking themselves into oblivion but the town centre too was also heaving every night with them. Their popular drinking haunts in those days were Paragon, King Edward, Masters Bar, Spencer Arms and White Lion that was in the old bus station. When the pubs closed they would make their way to Sky Line Club on the top of the BHS and Co-op building or Mecca that would become more famous in later years as LAs but has now been pulled down. We would hang about outside all these pubs waiting for chucking-out time. Then, as they started to pile out we would start hounding them for money, saying that we were orphans and giving them a real sob story. If they were with a girl they would always force them to give us money because they felt sorry for us. We soon cottoned on that if we changed our approach a bit we could make a fortune and so we used to dress in scruffy, torn clothes to look the part. One night we made so much money in coins that all our pockets were full to bursting. When we took it home to count it, we had over thirty pounds between four of us and in those days that was an absolute fortune. I remember the average wage for a week's work was about six pounds. We counted it out like little laughing devils and shared it out equally and it was whilst we were counting it that I had this absolutely brilliant idea.

"That's fucking brilliant," said Isse and we all started laughing.

The next day we went down to the local tat shop on

Hessle Road and we bought a wheelchair and some old leg irons that cripples used to wear in those days. That night Isse, Frankie and Terry pushed me around town in the wheelchair wearing the leg irons and at chucking out time the money just came pouring in. We were all making so much money that we almost did not know what to do with it or where to hide it. Even my Mum started to ask me if I would lend her some money and I was only about ten years old then. One of the things we spent our money on was clothes like Beatle Boots that were all the rage and jeans. Everybody wanted a pair of Levi's or Wrangler jeans because they were so expensive and you were "it" if you had a pair. It didn't take long though for the message to get out and soon all the local Hessle Road kids were out round town muscling in on our territory and most of them had bigger and meaner brothers than we had and so that put paid to that. It wasn't long though before we had other scams and were back in the money.

Our adventure and antics around town centre always led onto another and you would often meet other kids from other areas of Hessle Road on the midnight thieve as it were. Although you usually didn't mix with other kids from other areas of Hessle Road because there was a natural rivalry between areas and streets that usually emanated from bonfire night wood raiding when whole streets would raid each others piles of wood to steal it. In the run up to bonfire night sometimes hundreds of kids would meet to do battle on waste ground. Hordes of us would stand glaring at each other across no man's land and suddenly each would charge the other throwing bricks, bottles and whatever came to hand at each other. So you can imagine even after bonfire night had long gone, many a grudge between streets was carried throughout the year along with the scars and scores to settle.

One night after coming out of Dorchester Cinema we bumped into this actor we all knew as the one who played the Welsh teacher from the TV sit-com Please Sir and we got talking to him and were having a good laugh. He was doing a play at The New Theatre and took us in to watch and anyway it was a load of old shite so we left by the exit. Across the road we noticed a load of beer lorries parked behind some gates. It was the gates to the back of Hull Brewery and being young and naturally curious we took a closer look through the gates to see if there was anything worth nicking. The lorries were full of bottled beer in crates and so we climbed over the fence and helped ourselves. On the way home we got absolutely pissed and we all ended up sleeping in the bus shelter at the corner of Boulevard but it did give us an idea to make some money. The next night we went back to town with our two trusty old prams and when it got dark we climbed over the fence and into the Hull Brewery lorry park and passing the bottles through the fence we filled the two prams with bottles of beer. The next day we sold them around Marmaduke Street at half price and we had sold the lot within hours. The bloke who ran Criterion pub found out and said if we could get more he would buy it and so for the next two weeks we made regularly nightly trips into town and filled the two prams with beer and pushed them back down Hessle Road. For a couple of weeks it was just like the film 'Whisky Galore' down Marmaduke Street. Some of the beer we would keep for ourselves and a few of us would have a little party at the end of the street on a night and all get pissed. One night we were all so pissed we decided to play knock off ginger with the whole street. It was well gone one o'clock in the morning and Marmaduke Street was deathly quiet and everybody was in bed. Our plan was to for two of us to take one side of the street and the other two to take the other side of the street and on the count of three to run like hell down the street knocking on all or as many doors as we could. We reckoned we could make it from the end of the street to the top before anybody got out of bed to answer the door. Isse and me took up our positions on one side of the road and Terry and Frankie took up their positions on their side of the road. We all looked at each other.

"Ready?," I whispered across the road to Terry and Frankie, "One, two, three!" and with that we were off and running like hell, giving every door a good belt as we passed. Upstairs, lights were coming on all over the place. It took us about a minute to run down the whole street slamming on doors. We had almost finished as people started to appear on their doorsteps, just in time to spot us running around the corner and onto Hessle Road. We ran into a nearby shop doorway laughing and panting like exhausted greyhounds but just as we thought we had made a clean get away, a baying horde of people in pyjamas and slippers came racing around the corner after us.

"There they are!" a woman shouted and suddenly they were after us and we had a real chase on our hands. We pelted for our lives down Hessle Road in the dead of night with a riot of angry people screaming death after us. We bolted down the nearby Wellstead Street and none of us knew we could run so fast but they were still coming. All of a sudden our door-knocking prank did not seem such a good idea. We knew that if we were caught, we would get the beating of our lives and that is what kept us running. With all the commotion down Wellstead Street residents there were now coming out and shouting abuse at those chasing us and it wasn't long before someone was throwing punches. By this time we could see the sanctuary of Constable Street School and despite the spiked metal railings on top of the walls, we hit the walls running and scrambled over the spikes like agile monkeys. We all made it over safely except for Isse, who got his woolly jumper caught on one of the spikes and was left dangling like a trout on a fishing line. We hastily lifted him off but when we got him down all the stitching on his jumper had broken and the jumper went down to his feet.

"My mum's gonna kill me," he shouted at us. We ran through the black playgrounds to the Constable Street entrance and climbed out. We silently crept our way back down the dark end of Marmaduke Street and there were still lots of people out on the street and we could hear them swearing and talking. We hid out on to the waste ground there to catch our breaths and started laughing. We could hear cop car sirens over a nearby wall that looked out over to Wellstead Street and we climbed up and peak over. The whole street was swarming with coppers, cop cars and Police vans and we could hear what sounded like a riot going on. The next day we heard that those who lived down Wellstead had started fighting with those chasing us from Marmaduke Street and several had been arrested and some taken to hospital. Luckily no one seemed to be any the wiser that it was us four that had started it all. As for Isse's jumper he dumped it and told his mum someone had nicked it from school.

Our scam of robbing Hull Brewery was of course too good a thing to last. We all realised that it was just too easy and one night when we climbed over the fence they were waiting for us. We had managed only to pass a few bottles through the fence when four old codgers came charging out the darkness and started chasing Isse and me around the lorry-park shouting and swearing. But the blokes chasing us were way too old and we were dodging and generally running them ragged. We ran under the lorries and no matter how hard they tried they just couldn't catch us. It was just beginning to get fun when someone shouted from inside, "I've called the Police!" and we knew we had to make a quick exit. Outside Terry and Frankie started throwing beer bottles over the fences at them and shooting at them with peashooters and catapults. One bloke running after us slipped on the glass and another got a direct hit in the eye with a peashooter. Me and Isse climbed on top of

56

one of the parked beer lorries and managed from there to get onto a nearby roof that led to an alley on the back of the Dorchester Cinema and we climbed down and ran like hell. We met up with Terry and Frankie at the top of Hessle Road with our hearts pumping ten to the dozen. It had been another close shave that night but the only thing Hull Brewery managed to get was our two rusty old prams. We did go back after the dust had settled a few weeks later but they had put barbed wire on the gates and the lorry park was all lit up with an old crock of a night watchman armed with a torch and standing guard in a little wooden hut. Well, all good things come to an end but it had been a good little earner whilst it had lasted and it would be hard to replace such an easy money earner. If our two close shaves had been a close call, it in no way put us off our thieving or trouble making ways, although we never pulled a stunt like waking up the whole street again.

CHAPTER FIVE

As little kids growing up on Hessle Road if you had any ambition besides being a Thunderbird One pilot, it was to have your own bike. We all envied Barry Appleby because as I said he had a racing bike with five gears and although though he wasn't much to look at, all the girls used to crowd around him on a night and all they really wanted was a cross bar ride up the street. Sometimes Barry would take the girls the long way round coming back half an hour later all hot bothered and sweaty and that was another reason we all wanted a bike.

Often our little gang would go window shopping down Hessle Road. In those days there was no such thing as window shutters and all the shops would leave their lights on and the whole of Hessle Road would be lit up on a night and it would flood with bright light from one end of the road to the other. We would always end up outside of Kingston Cycles when it was on the corner of Strickland Street and just stare and dream at the brand spanking new racing bikes in the window. Isse Turner was the one who usually had money because he was the youngest in his big family, his Dad worked and his elder brothers all treated him but even he never had a racing bike. If there was one thing about Isse he would always share his money with us or if he bought sweets or fish and chips he would share them with us too. I suppose looking back we had always done a lot of stealing but over the next few years it became a sort of schoolboy occupation. And although there were a lot of thieves and dodgy people on Hessle Road we became so good at it one way or another that it wasn't long before we all had our own bikes.

If you had a bit about you, it was a great time to be a child on Hessle Road. On the run up to bonfire night most kids on Hessle Road went Penny for the Guy and with the road being so busy in the pubs every night you could earn a fortune. After Bonfire Night there was the run up to Christmas and New Year so you would go outside of the pubs and clubs and wish people "A Merry Christmas and Happy New Year". Usually you would get a few pennies or sometimes a couple of bob for your troubles and as the night wore on and as the pub customers became more drunk the more money you would get. If there had been a big trawler landing day the previous day Hessle Road would be heaving with taxis flying about everywhere, delivering drunken fishermen who had been paid off, to the pubs around the road and into the town. It might sound a bit too mercenary for children so young but we would often check the Hull Daily Mail for Trawler landings and plan our nights "on the scrounge" according to how many trawlers had landed. We were lucky that at the corner of Marmaduke Street was the Criterion Pub and that was always busy and full to the gunnels every night with fisher kids. The best time for scrounging money on Hessle Road was New Year's Eve. All the pubs opened till midnight and about half an hour before midnight every pub would empty and all the drunken grown-ups would pile into Fisherman's Bethal Church at the corner of the Boulevard for a big once a year, New Year's sermon, given by the vicar there. The church would get packed but I never knew what the vicar said because us kids weren't allowed in. But when the sermon finished and the new year bells had just started ringing and ships in the Humber were all blowing their fog horns, everybody piled out crying and just chucked piles of money endlessly at the crowd of waiting kids. It was every man for him self and there would be a mad scramble of kids chasing the coins and fighting with each other to get to the silver. You usually had to be big and quick but generally there was more than enough money being scrambled to go round but it was not unusual not only to collect "loadsa" money but a black eye or a fat lip as well for your trouble. You always had to be on the look out for coppers though because they would sometimes take your name and address because "Guy Fawking and Happy New Yearing" were considered begging so sometimes they would search you and confiscate your money. Generally though most coppers were good about it and just so long as you got out of their way whilst they patrolled and did not chuck it in their faces they would leave you alone. After Christmas and New Year was over it was always a bit of a lean time for our little gang but we hit on the idea of simply extending our activities 'Guy Fawking' to all the year round and would simply go begging outside of the pubs. I suppose begging is a bit of a harsh description and we saw it as "Out of season Guy Fawking". We would simply wait outside of pubs and ask the drunken fishermen for money and most of the time they would just throw us a pocketful of coins. Later on we developed this idea further and would buy bags of chips and fish cakes from Jacklin's fish shop on the corner of Marmaduke Street and offer them to the people coming out of pubs and they would give us money. We earned an absolute fortune doing that. That idea soon led to another where drinkers in the pubs would give us lists of things to get for them from the fish shops or Chinese takeaways. We would go to get their orders for them so that they did not have to wait in the queue after the pubs had chucked out at 11pm. I earned so much money one week that I hid it in the back of the toilet cistern in our outside toilet. When my mum went to toilet one day and pulled the chain all this money came cascading down and because she thought I had pinched it she kept it as a punishment, well so she said.

We also did other legitimate business as well. As they progressively pulled down more and more of Hessle

Road there were an awful lot of people moving out of their houses. There was lead from roofs you could make money on from the local rag yard down Eton Street. Old fireplaces too were in big demand and we would pull them out of the wall and sell them to Mellvile Salerooms. It was also staggering what some people would leave that you could sell. Antiques especially, old people used to leave lots of old vases, furniture and pictures you name it. Terry Cox, Isse Turner, Johnny Butler, Frankie Callis and me would go around all the empty houses sifting through what people had left. We would pile all the stuff we got out of the empty houses on to old prams and wheel them off down the road to Leslie's Antique shop. One really hot day we had a really good day in the empty houses down Coltman Street and our prams were full to the top with really good stuff. So full in fact that some of us were carrying stuff as well. It was such a hot day that we all took our tops off as we made our way down Hessle Road to Leslie's Antique Shop. By the time we got there we were absolutely tired out and we sat down on some old chairs outside the shop had put out on show.

"I'll go in," said Isse because he was usually the best haggler. The bloke who owned the shop was usually a real greedy sod and took advantage of us because we were kids. One day we had sold him two matching vases and he gave us five bob for them and the next day he had them in the window for twenty quid and sold them soon after. Anyway Isse came outside with this daft old bloke who was looking after the shop whilst the owner had gone out on a job. He went through all our stuff and offered us a fiver for the lot. Then rather sheepishly looked at us sitting on these chairs outside the shop and said. "They're not bad chairs them, I'll give you another fifteen quid for all four." We all looked at each other without saying a word and we all sort of shrugged our shoulders and the daft old git bought all four chairs off us that belonged to the shop. We took the money and quickly scarpered and it served the greedy bastard shop owner right for ripping us off with the vases.

When we were kids living down Hessle Road, many pastimes revolved around street games. Realio was a big game down Marmaduke Street especially during the long dark days of winter because you could hide better. In Realio you would have two teams and a terrace would act as the prison. One team would chase and the other team would be the chased. The chasers had to catch and hold onto the chased for ten-second and those caught would be held in the prison. The prison had to be defended because any of those being chased could release those in prison by running into the prison and shouting, "REALIO" and those captured could escape. More often than not this game could get a bit rough and often ended up in disputes, arguing or fighting especially if you disputed being caught so girls rarely played it. Many of the girls used to play double or triple ball against a wall, skipping or hopscotch. Some girls would often tuck their skirts into their knickers so it was nearly always worth watching. Tig was another game that was popular, where one person would be "It" and would have to chase the rest of the players to touch them and then they would be "It" and would have to chase you. I remember at Daltry Street School that we played this game a lot during playtime, though we modified our version of Tig to give it a degree of difficulty. All I will just say is that we called it "Cock Tig" and the idea was that you had to chase your mates around the playground and when you got hold of one of them you squeezed them between their legs as hard as you could and he was "It". Funnily enough not a lot of the girls wanted to play and our headmaster at Daltry Street juniors, Mr Lee, put a stop to it after Tony Brewer's Mum complained that Frankie Callis had squeezed her son's 'three piece suite' so hard that his balls swelled up. Just to reinforce his point Mr Lee gave us all six of the best in front of the school assembly as hard as he could on the arse. By this time having become something of an expert on getting my arse whacked, first by Miss Swift in infants and now in juniors, I have to say that Mr Lee had a really unique way to caning you and he didn't use a slipper or a cane. He would bend you over in front of him, put your head between his legs and give you a massive whack on the arse with his hand. Usually it was three whacks on each buttock or six on each if it was twelve of the best. Give me the slipper any time, not because it was less painful but it was just so undignified having your head between the headmaster's legs and your arse pointing at the whole school. Mind you it never stopped us playing 'Cock Tig' because it was just so much fun, we just played it on the quiet and to keep our secret safe we never let Tony Brewer play with us.

One night we had been playing realio and it had gone on for hours and everybody was getting really angry because there was a lot of cheating going on. It was about 10pm and Stuttering Joe came out. "If you lot don't f,f,f,f,fuck off, I'm g,g,g,g,going for the police."

"Oh get in, ya stuttering old bastard," we shouted back at him and we all started jeering. Anyway it wasn't long before Joe was knocking on neighbours doors complaining and they started calling in their kids. Before long everybody had gone home and only Isse and me were left. We retreated to a corner shop doorway and it wasn't long before we were planning our vengeance on Stuttering Joe for spoiling our game. We left it for a while for things to quieten down and then we got some rope off a nearby lamppost that the girls had been using for a swing. We crept up to Stuttering Joe's door and tied the rope to the door handle. If I can just remind you that Stuttering Joe lived next door to my Uncle Harold who also stuttered and they both hated each other. So we tied Joe's door handle to my Uncle Harold's door handle and knocked as hard as we could on both doors. Then, Isse and me stood there and waited. It wasn't long before Stuttering Joe came to the door and started pulling and shouting.

"Who the f,f,f,f,fuck is that?" Then my Uncle Harold started pulling to open his door.

"Is that you Joe, get off my f,f,f,f,fucking door, ya stuttering bastard." Isse and me were banging on both doors with Stuttering Joe and my Uncle Harold shouting abuse at each other thinking each was holding their door. As soon as we heard footsteps coming from the back ways, after they had both gone out of their back doors and were coming round to the front, Isse and me ran down a nearby alley and watched Joe and my Uncle Harold come face to face outside. Then my Uncle Harold punched Joe.

"Knock on my f,f,f,f,fucking door would ya?" shouted Harold and they started rolling about in the street. It wasn't long before lights were coming on and people were coming out in their curlers and pyjamas to watch. Fortunately the situation was brought to an abrupt end when another of Uncle Harold's neighbours Mr Appleby rolled up his bedroom window.

"Do you two soft bastards know what time it is," he shouted down at them. " I have to get up in the morning for work while you two lazy bastards stink in bed. If I have to come down there I'll put both you bastards in hospital."

Even though Isse and me were still only about twelve or thirteen we rarely went home until the early hours and would often hang about the street talking into the night. During the late hours Marmaduke Street had its own nocturnal night creatures in the form of people you never saw during the day that would come out at night just like hedgehogs or bats. One of the many nocturnal creatures was a middle age bloke who always chose the middle of the night to take his very old dog for a walk. There was a rumour down the street that he only came out late at night because of what he used to get up to with his dog and that's all I want to say on the matter. Us kids only knew him by his first name of Peter but somehow he had gained the nickname of Peter Pudding Head or Pudding Head Peter. Now I cannot explain the local history of what I am going to impart to you, as history was never my strong point at school. You may choose to believe me or not but apparently on Hessle Road those known for certain perverted sexual activities with animals such as dogs were known as "Pudding Heads". Maybe if someone would like to take that question to Hull University's history department they might get a definitive answer as to what a "Pudding Head" is but as I say I do not have one. So now at least you will understand why we called him Peter Pudding Head and why we thought it funny and also why Peter did not like being called a Pudding Head. Peter had a habit of coming to sit with Isse and me on the step of the shop doorway for a friendly chat about school and especially about girlfriends. There were an awful lot of weirdos on Hessle Road in those days that seemed to take a great interest in the sex life of teenagers and seemed to be concerned that we were getting our share and that we should share our experiences with them. It might have been one way they got their kicks or showed true fatherly interest but I suspect it was the former. Either way it did make life a bit more interesting for us kids because we could have a laugh teasing these pervs and usually that would end in a good chase with them screaming obscenities as they chased us down the road. Peter Pudding Head was one of many innocent pervs down our street and the conversation would always start in the same way. He would give us a smile, show his black teeth and go all bashful and coy as he came towards us.

"Hello boys, you're out late." I suppose most children today would run like hell when someone looking like Peter approached them but somehow we always felt safe. Even though we were still quite young we were streetwise and could to a degree handle ourselves and we were hungry for fun.

"You don't mind if I sit down?" he would say and he would sit down on the step with his dog taking a seat next to him.

"Hello Peter," we would reply with a slight snigger under our breaths.

"Going for a walk Pete?" said Isse.

"Have you been to school today then lads?" Pete would ask us in an inquisitive voice. "Bet you've both got nice girlfriends." And then we would get him going by describing some recent fictional sexual adventure.

"Yeah," I replied. "Me and Isse got these two girls in Constable Street playground last night, didn't we Isse?"

"Yeah, Yeah," Isse joined in. "Took them in school and wha-hey! Jackpot!"

Peter's eyes would come out of his head as he waited for the intimate details.

"What did you? What did you do?" he demanded all excited.

"You know Pete," said Isse, "give 'em a good old seeing too, din't we Ian?"

"Are you kidding," I piped up, "A right good old seeing to." And then I asked him slowly. "Have you got a girlfriend Pete?"

"Bet you've had loads of girlfriends 'ain't you Pete?" Isse said, sniggering.

"I did when I was your age," said Pete with a big dirty smile and he started laughing all lecherously.

"Come on then tell us more, what happened with these girls?" he said getting all eager and hot under the collar.

"We picked 'em up outside of the off license last night," I replied, with my voice rising to a higher note of excitement as each word came out. "Isse went in and bought a couple of bottles of mild and we went in

Constable Street School."

"Yeah! Yeah!" asked Peter with growing excitement, "and then what did you do?"

"Well what do you think Peter?" said Isse obviously.

"Did you kiss them?" said Peter with some urgency now in his voice.

"Course we did," said Isse loudly, "and then we got down to some serious stuff. "They had miniskirts on, oh, you should have seen the legs on them Peter. Legs with big thick riding thighs." Then Isse suddenly started talking really slow and Peter was hanging on his every word like a hungry man.

"She was gagging and I put my hand on her leg and..." Isse breathed heavily.

"Ooooooh ya dirty little sods," said Peter almost beside himself. "Go on! Go on!"

"We were at it for hours," Isse told him, " weren't we Ian?"

"Phew are you kidding, absolutely hours." I retorted emphatically. "Like four rabbits eh Isse?"

"You what," announced Isse. "They were absolutely knackered by the time we finished with them. We gave 'em what for eh Ian."

"What about you Peter, you must have had a few in Constable Street playground?" I asked him outright.

"Woooooh, are you kidding? But that was a few years ago now," said Peter with a big mucky smile.

"You like girls don't you Peter?" Isse teased him.

"Yes, but I don't get many chances these days though, not like you two mucky buggers," he said sniggering. "Not like during the war when all the blokes were away, the girls were gagging for it round here, you what," he said with a swoon. "I spent more time between lasses' legs than a fanny doctor."

At this point Isse and me would slowly start to get up and as soon as we were on our feet and sure that Peter could not reach us, we would deliver our usual punch line.

"So why do they call you Pudding Head?" we would both suddenly shout at him and run like hell.

"Ya pair of bastards!" he would shout back, "I'm not a fucking Pudding Head!"

CHAPTER SIX

As I have stated previously but can't emphasise enough, is that one of the most prized possessions any kid on Hessle Road could have, was a bike. Not just any bike I hasten to add but one of those lean, mean racing machines with a five-gear derailleur, racing handle bars and a razor sharp ball-busting racing seat. Now that really was a machine and the only place you ever saw them on Hessle Road was hanging in the windows of Kingston Cycles at a price that was way out of the reach of the pockets of most parents on Hessle Road. I can count on two fingers the number of kids down Hessle Road who I knew that had such a machine. As I said, one was Barry Appleby and the other was a kid who I didn't know but who I regularly saw riding it up and down the road, much to my great envy. There was great kudos attached to having such a bike and it was a magnet for the local girls. Until I got wise most of the mobility in my childhood came from bogie making. Bogies are basically a plank of wood connected to a set of pram wheels at each end. The front end wheels on the bogie would have wheels that swivelled around on a bolt so you could sort of steer it with your feet or a piece of rope whilst your mates pushed you. If you had a really upmarket bogie you would have half an orange box nailed to the plank that you could sit in as you blazed down the road taking your life and the lives of others in your hands. With no brakes to stop you, often you found yourself travelling at 'break a bone' speed with only the soles of your shoes to act as brakes. And all too often you would end up crashing into parked cars or kerbs and taking the skin off your legs as you skidded on your arse along the road. It went without saying that such a peasant mode of transport did not impress the good looking, local 'totty' who would not be seen dead riding on the back of your bogie with their legs wrapped around you to stop them falling off. The only girl we could get on our gang's bogie was known by the big boys in Marmaduke Street as 'Polo' after the mints and I am not going to explain why she was called Polo, just use your imagination. Until we all got bikes of our own it was left to Barry Appleby to have all the fun and we had to make do with the female cast offs, too ugly to qualify for a ride on Barry's cross bar, like Polo.

In those days there was only one way really to get the bike of your dreams for the likes of us and that was to steal one. The down side to that was everybody would know where you had got it from if you were suddenly seen riding a racing bike. The coppers also soon had their eye on you if the bike you were riding did not match the scruff riding it, if you know what I mean. It had been to the cost of quite a few local kids that they had been caught riding stolen bikes. In those days there was no such thing as cautions off the coppers and if you were caught stealing three times you nearly always got three years in borstal. Oh yes, they did not piss ball around with kids in those days like they do today. When coppers walked down our street the whole street would go quiet so you didn't attract their attention because they thought nothing of searching your house with or without a warrant. So as kids our main problem was how to steal a bike and be able to ride it like it was our own without fear that the coppers were going to nick us. It did not take us long to work how we could do this and when we did there was not a bike that was safe anywhere in Hull. Nearly all good bikes in those days would have a frame number stamped somewhere on the frame, usually it was just underneath the frame near the peddles. So if you got caught on a good nicked bike it was a foregone conclusion you were done for. It was no good filing off the number because that was equally a sign of guilt. What we used to do was to get a bike frame from the ragman for a few bob and then go around nicking bikes, stripping them and then transferring all the parts to our frame. That way it did not even matter if the bike was locked up, because all we wanted was the parts. Once we spotted a really good racing bike, we would steal it if it wasn't locked up but if it was locked up, we would just strip it clean of its parts in situ. We were able to strip a bike of its parts faster than a hyena stripping a carcass. The only tools that we needed for this task was an adjustable spanner and a pair of pliers and even the tools we would nick from Boyes' tool department. In those days Boyes had quite an extensive range of tools at very reasonable prices I might add, and as it was just around the corner from Marmaduke Street it was very handy for shoplifting. It was rare for Boyes not to have the stuff in you needed for nicking bikes but on the odd occasions they did not, there was always Woolies a few hundred yards down the road. I preferred Boyes myself as the tools from Woolies in those days were very cheap and nasty and I had been in the middle of stripping many a bike when the spanner snapped. It is so infuriating when you can only get a job half done. I am not surprised Woolies eventually went bust whilst Boyes still sails on down Hessle Road.

One day Frankie Callis, myself, Johnny Butler and Isse Turner had been out on 'bike nicking patrol' down near Wassand Street Arms, a pub at the end of Wassand Street, which is still there today. Most people in those days would usually go for a drink after work and leave their bikes chained up to the lampposts outside. Most of the bikes you saw were not worth nicking because they were old, rusty or did not have racing bike parts on them. It's not that we were choosy or anything but if you were going to take the risk of stripping a bike you at least wanted to get some good parts for your efforts and risk. I mean if you got caught you didn't want to get a good hiding for trying to nick some rusting, old bone-shaker. Well we had been doing our reconnaissance on Wassand Arms for days and night after night the same old rubbish was being left locked up outside. Some of them were hardly worth the cost of the bike lock they were using to lock them with. We were just about to give it up as a bad job when this bloke came bombing up on this top notch racing bike, pulled up and locked his racer up to a lamppost. For a couple of seconds the bloke stood back like he was admiring it and took a moment to wipe some mud off the back mudguard. He seemed almost in love with it and I don't blame him, this bike was the dog's bollocks and it had a ten-speed derailleur, yes, that's what I said, a ten-speed derailleur. Ten-speed derailleur racing bikes were like the stuff of legends for kids on Hessle Road and they didn't even have them in the window at Kingston cycles. It also had saddlebags and two water bottles on the handlebars. This bloke took his bike riding as seriously as we took nicking them. It looked brand new and I would not have been surprised if he had just road it out of the Kingston Cycles bike shop. I could see everybody's eyes popping out their heads and just drooling to get stuck in.

"I'm having the wheels," demanded Johnny Butler suddenly.

"I want the wheels," Frankie started arguing back.

"You've already got some wheels!" Johnny glared back at him.

"Alright, you can have 'em," Frankie answered him back and pushed him.

Johnny Butler punched Frankie in the face and before we knew where we were they were scrapping like a couple of scalded cats on the floor. A minute later and the bloke who owned the bike came out of the pub, took one look at them fighting and came across the road and pulled Frankie and Johnny apart. Just like the song really. The man had them both by the scruff of the neck.

"What's going on then?" he shouted at both of them. Frankie's nose was bleeding and Johnny's face and eye were all red and bruised. The man made them both shake hands and told us all to go home. What a nice bloke I thought and it seemed a pity we were going to nick his bike. We all walked quietly down Wassand Street knowing that if the fight had not have broken out we would have probably all been caught right in the middle of stripping the bloke's bike. Anyway we watched this bloke just get something out of his saddlebags and then go back into the pub.

"That was close. We'll come back tomorrow," I said quietly, "And you two can toss up for the wheels."

Come the next night the four of us laid in wait on 'hill of bricks' across the road on a building site like soldiers waiting to ambush the enemy. Now stripping a bike is a specialist job and we had stripped enough chained-up bikes to know you had to be quick. Our record was about four minutes to get the whole bike stripped leaving only the frame chained up. Each one of us would take a specified part of the bike to strip and we would all be on edge like troops waiting to go over the top. Eventually the bloke with the mean machine we were waiting for came peddling down Wassand Street. I could hear him whistling as he climbed off the bike and felt sure that he would not be whistling when he came out. Anyway he locked up his bike at the same lamppost and the very second the bloke's back disappeared through the door of the pub, we were off our blocks and running full pelt across the road. Off came the wheels, next the seat, the peddles, chain, derailleur, handle bars and bottles, saddle bags, mudguards and even the brakes. In four minutes flat we were off and running like whippets across the building site into the next street, which was Walcott Street, carrying our booty. I cannot remember how many times we stripped bikes like this but we always wondered what the owner's reaction would be when he came out of the pub after a couple of quiet pints to find what was left of his bike chained to the lamppost. But I'm sure you'll understand why we never hung around long enough to find out.

Once we had got the frame and the parts for our bike it was no good putting the whole thing together on an old tatty bike frame. So that meant stripping and painting the frame so it looked the business if we were going to outshine Barry Appleby. Most people from Hessle Road will know of the store Setams, it was like an emporium that seemed to sell almost everything in the world you could want. Inside, the shop was piled to the gunnels with all sorts of stuff. It sold everything from spray paint for bikes to cutlery, pots and pans, you name it, Setams had it. Before it moved many years ago to the corner of Boulevard, Setams used to be on the corner of Madeley Street and it just had everything you could want for building a bike. The two blokes who ran it were either daft or not bothered about the amount of stuff that got nicked. It was like a general pastime on Hessle Road for local kids to go stealing from Setams. A good deal of stuff was always piled outside on counters and that was always an easy get-away. We always shopped for bike spray paint at Setams as they kept it outside. The gang would all help each other to do up their bikes. Johnny Butler was a real dab hand at fixing bikes and I became something of an expert myself. Any bike parts we did not need we would sell or make up into another bike and then sell the whole bike. Anyway it was not long before Barry Appleby's reign as the cross bar king of Marmaduke Street came to an end and each of us regularly had a bird on the cross bar for the round trip to Division Road cemetery. It was a case of totty on tap and "fill ya boots mother". It gave us a whole new perspective on life for the gang to have mobility and we would cycle everywhere. One day we even cycled to

Withernsea and slept on the beach. On the way back we must have stopped at every village corner shop and ransacked it. By the time we got home we had bags full of chocolates and lemonade. That evening after nicking a four-man tent from Boyes we camped out with four girls and had a party in a small wooded area down Coltman Street called Acko's.

As time went on most of the kids down Marmaduke acquired bikes using our methods and bikes were disappearing from factory bike sheds all down Hessle Road. It was not long before the coppers at Gordon Street noticed that the scruffs down Marmaduke Street all had nice bikes and they raided on mass a load of houses including Frankie Callis's and mine. They took all the frame numbers off our bikes and said they would be back in a few days. Of course they couldn't prove anything because we had taken precautions and had got our own bikes stamped with frame numbers just in case some thieving sod nicked ours. After all you can't be too careful can you with all the thieves down Hessle Road at that time. When the coppers came back to reluctantly give us the all-clear, the sergeant's face was red with anger because he knew one way or another we had nicked the bikes and told us so but he couldn't prove a thing. My mum was not too pleased at having the house raided but even she had seen that I had bought the bike frame and built the bike myself so she gave the coppers a mouthful for picking on us downtrodden kids just because we were poor. Up the revolution, eh Mum?

It is strange how once you got something you always wanted, that the novelty quickly wore off and that's the way it was with our bike phase. But it still didn't stop us stealing bikes and most other things that weren't nailed own. One really hot day about twenty of us from Marmaduke Street had gone to the annual open day at Newland Homes down Cottingham Road. It was the real posh part of town and there were bikes everywhere parked outside and most were not locked and we all casually helped ourselves to one each and road them into town and ended up going swimming in Jelly Fish Bay. For anybody who does not know where Jelly Fish Bay is, it is on the dock that sits on the back of where Viking Radio is today. It is a wonder swimming in that cess pit that we didn't catch something but all the kids off Hessle Road used to go there for a swim especially at night.

Anyway, when we finished we chucked all the bikes into the bay because many were just too good to take home and the coppers would have had a field day. I remember one of the younger kids who had come with us was determined that he was not going to dump his bike in the bay and he was holding on to it for dear life. We could all understand his thinking because the bike was just beautiful and almost brand new. Normally he would probably never get to ride, let alone own such a bike. He was just too young to understand that the moment the coppers saw him riding it on Hessle Road they would nick him and then he would spill the beans and they would come for the rest of us. Despite all of us arguing with him he was determined that he was going to keep the bike. One of the bigger boys who was with us was Jeff Butler, my mate Johnny Butler's older brother and he relented and said that the young lad could keep the bike and threatened to kick anybody's head in if they touched him or the bike. Although Jeff was a hard case and looked even more ferocious because of his hair lip, none of us were ever likely to agree with that. We'd all chucked our bikes into the bay and there was no way any of us were going to get into bother with the coppers just because that tosser had got caught riding one. In those days nicking bikes was a very serious crime and we had nicked about twenty that day and we would have all got sent down the road without question if we got caught.

Jeff went over to the lad and inspected his bike.

"Bloody hell," he said with a big swoon, "I don't blame you, it's a nice bike. I wish I had kept mine now. Let's have a go then." With that the lad let Jeff ride it around the bay and when he came back on it, he climbed off, smiled at the young kid but then threw the bike into the bay. The young kid started crying his eyes out.

"Shut ya mouth!" Jeff growled at him, "If I hadn't thrown it in, they would have kicked your head in, then thrown you and your bike in."

Jeff could have just slapped him and thrown his bike in but he was not like that and we all liked and trusted Jeff because of the way he was. Besides his hair lip Jeff had big ears and we all used to take the piss out of him and he used to make us all laugh because he used to make fun of himself and his big ears. There were far too many bullies on Hessle Road who liked to throw their weight around, especially with us little kids but Jeff, although a hard case was not one of them. He was right about one thing though, none of us would have let the lad walk away with that bike and we would have thrown him in the bay with the bike to teach him a lesson. That's the way it was on Hessle Road and there was no room for fools in our gang.

Over the years I have seen all sorts of stolen stuff being dumped into Jelly Fish Bay and bikes got dumped there in great numbers after we'd finished riding them for the day. In later years we would move up to stealing motorbikes, motor scooters and the odd car, some of which also went into the bay after a joy ride. The bottom of Jelly Fish Bay must be a real Steptoe's dream.

CHAPTER SEVEN

If you wanted fun there was always something going on down Marmaduke Street and as we all grew older so the later we stayed out on the street. One summer night when Mike Fox was home from borstal we were all playing football in the street. We didn't usually allow Mike to play with us in the street because he had a tendency to stink to high heaven, which scared the girls away but it was his football and we couldn't really argue with that. Anyway 'nutty Mike' as we called him was bragging to my older brother Colin about how many pigeons he had. If anything pushed all my brother's buttons it was the word pigeon. My brother was a pigeon lunatic. Whilst most of us would spend our time in more productive pastimes like stealing, he spent his spare time climbing about in the old shipping warehouses in the town trying to catch pigeons and breaking into corn wagons to steal feed corn to feed his precious birds. I mean what a waste of time stealing pigeons and seed corn. Why my brother couldn't spend his time in more productive ways like the rest of us and steal something useful was beyond me. He used to train his pigeons for racing and selling to other local pigeon freaks. Sometimes he would sell a pigeon knowing that as soon as the new owner let it out it would come straight back to his loft and he would sell it all over again. Anyway Mike took us all down the back alley and into his back yard for us to see his pigeons. It was a right run down, sad affair of a pigeon loft and was in fact the old coal bunker and a bit of a shed combined into one with the front covered in chicken wire and it smelt and looked like it had never been cleaned out. The pigeons looked in no better state than the loft and there were more feathers on the floor than on the pigeons. He had twenty chickens lodging in the loft as well so the smell was only slightly more tolerable than Mike. The pigeon and chicken shit was about six inches deep and it was starting to cake on the soles of our shoes. Anyway my brother reckoned his pigeons were poor excuses for birds and told him so and Mike said he wasn't breeding them for racing but for eating. I could see the thought of someone eating pigeons did not go down very well with my brother. But if you had asked me I couldn't think of any better use for pigeons, since the only thing my brother's pigeons seemed to be good at was shitting on the clothes on our washing line, much to my mum's constant irritation.

"What are the chickens for?" I asked nutty Mike.

"My Dad sells them to the Arabs down Waverley Street. He gets thirty-bob a piece." replied Mike. "He makes a fortune out of them because they like to kill them themselves but they can't get them alive. They make chicken soup out of them. That's all them Arabs eat, chicken soup."

At that precise moment the back gate opened and Mike's Dad, old man Foxy came into the back yard from the alley pushing his old pram full of junk, including a television on the top, that he had bought at the sale rooms.

"You don't know anyone who wants a telly do you boys?" he asked us all with his usual rejoin. "I see Mike's showing you his birds." Old man Foxy pushed the pram into a corner of the yard and tied one of the wheels to a drainpipe with some feeble string as if it would stop anybody stealing it. He then started to cripple himself, carting his junk into the house, huffing and coughing as he struggled to carry the television through the back door.

"Well give us a bloody hand then," he shouted at Mike. "And make sure you feed them chickens, the ab-dabs are buying six tomorrow." Mike turned around and looked at us with a crazy smile on his face.

"See I told you. We're gonna be rich."

Mike always did live on a different planet to the rest of us and I suppose if Marmaduke Street had been a village Mike would have fitted in really well as the village idiot. And as for his hopes of becoming rich as Hessle Road's first 'chicken Baron', they were about to be dashed by the cruel hand of fate - and me and my mates. Just listening to Mike Fox and I had done a quick mental calculation, twenty chickens at thirty bob a piece, that was thirty quid. Just looking at the state of the pigeon loft and the conditions the chickens were being kept in and it looked to me like money for doing nothing. Just feed them and flog them but where would we keep them I asked myself? There was no chance my brother would let me keep any chickens in his precious pigeon loft and now the more I thought about it the more problems it presented. It was a pity though because it sounded like a right good little money-spinner. I then had another more simple idea of how I could make even more money out of chickens by cutting out the whole of the chain of supply and the issue over logistics. The more I thought about it the more I knew it was a brilliant idea. All I would have to do was sell the chickens to the Arabs, which would be simple enough as being half-caste I knew most of them anyway because they had known my Dad. It was a brilliant business model I came up with and I could not help giving myself a mental pat on the back. No outlay to buy the chickens, no hassle of keeping them, no feeding costs and no smelly chicken shit to clean up. It was a brilliant idea, just brilliant. With absolutely no costs I could make even more money. But I can hear you asking already, how is Ian going to do it? Simple really, a good businessman always lets others do the hard work for him and that's exactly what I was going to do. I would just steal all Foxy's chickens…

It was dark that night about 11 pm and by midnight apart from a few 'midnight snoggers' dotted about in doorways, all was calm and quiet in Marmaduke Street as Isse, me, Frankie and Terry ran in silence down the street and stealthily ducked into Foxy's terrace and crept silently up to the front of his house. We guessed that the chickens would make a lot of noise as we grabbed them and that old man Foxy and nutty Mike would be out of their stinky pits very quickly to see what was going on. So first we screwed up their front door with about ten, shit big, six-inch screws. Then we climbed over the back way and did the same to their back door.

We had brought four big sacks to put the chickens in. It was pitch black in the yard and we could hardly see a thing. Terry had brought his big torch and as soon as we tore the wire off the front of the pigeon loft the pigeons went into a panic and started flapping and flying out of the loft. In the commotion Terry Cox slipped on the chicken shit and pulled Isse and Frankie down as well. They were all covered in chicken shit and by now the chickens were squawking and making more noise than a burglar alarm but one by one we manage to get them into the sacks. By then however, the lights were starting to go on in Foxy's house and he was rattling the back door, trying to get out and looking through the kitchen window.

"Quick Mike go the front way," we heard old man Foxy shout. We had just about got the last chicken in the sack when we heard nutty Mike.

"Dad the front door's stuck!"

"Are ya fucking daft, try unlocking it. Are you a fucking retard or what?" Did Foxy love his son or what? " Hurry up shit-for-brains they're nicking the fucking chickens!"

"Hey it might be a fox Dad!" we heard Mike say.

"Shut up silly bastard!" old man Foxy shouted at him. "How many foxes do you see carrying a torch!" And then he started shouting through the back door. "I've got my baseball bat and I'm gonna fucking kill ya when I get my hands on ya." Old man Foxy couldn't knock the skin off a rice pudding and none of us were scared with his bravado.

"We've got a gun you old bastard!" Terry shouted back in a heavily disguised voice and with that we threw the chickens over the wall and were back in my yard in a few minutes. We put the chickens in my brother's pigeon loft just until morning.

"Phew, you three stink," I said holding my breath.

Terry, Isse and Frankie were covered in chicken shit from head to foot and would have some explaining to do when they got home...

The next morning we were up early and we flogged all the chickens to the Arabs down Waverley Street but the greedy sods haggled us down to a quid a piece because they knew we needed rid of them. Even so twenty quid for one night's work wasn't bad for four twelve-year-old kids. Five pounds each was a king's ransom in those days and we spent the rest of the day in town gorging on Wimpy and chips, choc-ices and lots of chocolate.

If you think this was the end of the chicken episode you would be wrong as there were more foul deeds to come, if you will forgive the pun. By the time we got home later that day, who should be walking down the street but old man Foxy and Mike. For the first time ever he was not pushing his old pram. Instead, both of them were straining on a long rope tied around the neck of this monster of an Alsatian dog with a big studded collar and chunks of fur missing from all over its body. It looked like the Hound of The Baskervilles as it kept turning round and snapping at them. It was a real effort for old man Foxy and Mike just to hold onto the rope and try to control it.

"Heel Caesar! Heel Caesar!" they both shouted but the dog just turned round and barked and snapped at them and then tried to take a bite out of Mike's leg.

"Hey up Foxy. What ya got there?" I shouted at him.

"It's a guard dog, that is going to protect our property," he announced proudly. "Last night someone nicked our chickens."

"That's terrible Foxy," said Isse feigning outrage, "they'll nick anything these days."

"Well just let anybody try getting in our yard now," growled Foxy, "and Caesar will tear their throats out." By this time the dog was getting so unruly it was pulling both of them around like rag dolls with Mike trying desperately to keep out of range of its teeth.

"Dad! Dad! Let's go, I can't hold on much longer." With that, Caesar suddenly dragged them both off down the street and as they clung to the rope for dear life a group of onlookers had to jump out of the way of the dog's snapping teeth.

All that night the whole street was kept awake with this hound howling and barking and how there was not a riot I don't know. A 'lynch mob' of neighbours in dressing gowns and pyjamas laid siege outside Foxy's house baying for blood but Foxy was not daft enough to go out. By morning though, what few windows Foxy had left in his house had all been put through and someone had stolen his famous pram, cut the wheels off and tied the remains to the top of a lamppost like some sinister medieval warning. The next day Foxy surfaced in the street carrying a sack full of chickens and running the gauntlet of abuse from neighbours who had been kept awake all night. It occurred to us that Foxy was obviously re-stocking with chickens now that he felt sure that his trusty hound Caesar could protect his coop. A quick glance over Fox's back yard wall was met with a ferocious barrage of barking, snarling and growling and it was clear anyone daring to enter his yard would not get out alive after that dog had finished with them. It was certainly not a friendly animal towards trespasser or owner alike and that gave us an idea, a mischievous one of course. With lots of people being cleared out of Hessle Road as they pulled down the houses many people left their pets and so there were stray cats everywhere that had become almost wild. So that night we collected about four of them in a sack and threw the sack over Foxy's back yard wall. The dog started barking and growling like mad and it sounded like all hell had been let loose in the back yard. Neighbours windows were up and they were all shouting abuse about the noise. The cats broke into the chicken coop and there were feather flying left, right and centre. We listened from behind the wall and heard Mike and old man Foxy stumble out of the back door shouting and screaming.

"Dad! Dad! Fucking cats in the loft!"

"Let Caesar off the rope!" Old man Foxy shouted and with that Mike let the growling, snarling hound off the rope. "Catssss! Caesar, Catssss!" Mike snarled at the dog and pointed to the loft but instead of the dog going after the cats we heard Mike scream and the sound of dustbins being tossed about as the dog turned on Mike and Old Man Foxy. They both bolted quickly back into the house screaming at the top of their voices as the dog chased after them. We could hear absolute mayhem coming from inside the house with bangs and crashes and Mike and old man Foxy screaming blue murder.

"Fucking hit it with something," old man Foxy screamed at Mike.

The next day no one saw Foxy or Mike but a dog van and several Police cars laid siege to Foxy's house like in a scene from one of those James Cagney films. The only thing that was missing was the dog shouting from the window, "Come and get me coppers," and someone with a loud hailer asking the dog to give himself up. After some reluctance the dog warden inched his way into the house and the last we saw of the hound of the Baskervilles was a dog warden wrestling the animal out of the back yard on one of those special leashes attached to a long pole. The

Fox family were not spotted in the street until the evening when an ambulance stopped at the end of their terrace and Mike and old man Foxy climbed out all black and blue with one arm each in a sling and old man Foxy in a wheel chair. After his bad experience in the chicken business I don't think Foxy every dabbled in the business again.

A few days later, as often happened, Mike's holiday from borstal was cut short after his Dad caught him breaking into the gas and electric meters and called the Police. It would later transpire that it had actually been old man Foxy who had done the meters and blamed it on to his son but Mike not being a full shilling, if you will forgive another pun, took the rap. Oh happy days.

CHAPTER EIGHT

Sex education was non existent in my early childhood at school on Hessle Road and then one day something dawned on me when I was about six years old. It was one of those Eureka moments that all children have and they always end up asking the same question. I remember running up to my mother all excited at having a question that would make me look like a clever little boy. She was cleaning the fire place grating on her knees in the living room and was a bit flustered because the cat had had diarrhoea all night and had shit all over the living room and had stank the house out. Tiddles was my cat and was special because he only had half a tail and I always liked to give him plenty of treats but I don't think those rotten fish heads I got from Wilkinson's Fish house across the street had quite agreed with him.

"Mummy? Mummy?" I said loudly, trying to get her attention.

She looked up at me quite startled with smudges of cinder dust on her cheek and she blew a wisp of hanging hair out of her face and if not for the Capstan full strength fag hanging from the corner of her mouth, she looked just like Cinderella. "Look I'm busy will you fuck off outside and play"

"But Mummy, I've got a question."

She rolled her eyes and took a big drag on her fag. "Oh go on then."

"Where do we come from?" I asked inquisitively.

I will remember her response to this very day and she looked at me all startled and thinking back that should have been the signal to, "Fuck off outside and play," as quickly as possible but alas I lingered waiting for an answer with a big daft smile on my face.

"Shut up you dirty little bugger!" she snapped and with a speed that would have put Muhammad Ali to shame she cuffed me with a lighting right hook across the lug hole that came out of nowhere and I ran off with my ear glowing like a traffic stop light having ducked too late. I gathered from her reaction that there was a bit more to this babies business than the stork flying them in from the North Pole or being found in a box on the doorstep but was intrigued what all the secrecy was about. I remember thinking at the time of my mother's lightening right, "What was all that about?" and "That bloody hurt you old bag!" and come to think of it, it wasn't Cinderella you looked like after all but one of the ugly sisters and having learned my lesson I never asked my mother that question again. From that day forward I would be on a holy mission to seek out the truth and was determined to investigate the subject some more and get to the bottom of this strange mystery about where we came from though it would sometime later after my mother's short shrift of my question before I gave it anymore thought after I came across the mysterious case of the motorbike seat. Sometimes we used to take a shortcut to Daltry Street School and cut into Strickland Street down the bottom end of Wassand Street where Sam Allan Ltd were demolishing some of the houses that had already been partially demolished by German Luftwaffe Ltd a few years earlier and now left the two streets merged into each other at that point. That particular morning I noticed that some boys on the way to school would take the opportunity to sit on this motorbike that the owner use to leave parked on a back wall next to the fish house down there. There was quite a frenzy of activity around the motorbike and some boys were furiously pushing each other and arguing about who was next up to sit on it. Now I could quite understand the attractions of wanting to pretend that you were bombing down the road showing off to your friends but I got the distinct impression that there was some other motive to sitting on this motorbike, motives that went beyond innocent boyhood games. Having had my attention attracted, I stood there watching for a moment or two and my curiosity was further aroused. Some of the boys seemed to get great pleasure by climbing astride on the motor bike seat and sliding up and down on the seat. I could not see the attraction myself of such an odd past time but they do say that you should not knock something until you have tried it yourself. So one day, totally gripped by my childhood curiosity, I climbed aboard the motorbike myself when no one was looking to see what the fascination was all about and have to admit to quite a pleasurable sensation in rather a strange place. So nice was the experience in fact that I have to admit that I went to school that way almost every day after that and took a regular place in the queue of boys getting their early morning thrill on that motor bike and would often be late for school, sometimes very late. I remember in later years I relayed my experiences with the motorbike seat to my mate Terry Cox and he confessed to me how he used to enjoy sliding down lampposts and described the same pleasurable feelings as I got sitting on the motorbike. The motorbike having long since been moved by the owner, no doubt to repair the seat, I decided to try the lamppost method as described by my mate Terry Cox but alas it was not for me. I tried it once but only managed to get a painful Chinese burn on my willy. Terry said I had probably slid down too fast and I should leave my underpants and trousers on next time but I gave that one up as a bad job. I suppose it is experiences like that with motorbike seats and sliding down lampposts that get you thinking and you naturally graduate on to other activities in the lower bodily regions and no longer need motorbike seats or lampposts.

Though on behalf of me and my young school friends, I would like to belatedly thank the owner of that motorbike for making a lot of little boys very happy on their way school.

During my early years when I was still trying to figure out what certain bodily equipment was for, you heard all sorts of stories about what grown-up men and women get up to in the dark hours. It seemed to me too dastardly to even think about and I felt sure these stories were being made up. I had to admit though to a strange pleasurable sensation similar to sitting on that motorbike seat in the willy region whenever me and my friends played kiss-cats with the girls at play time. It was also difficult not to notice how a particular part of the anatomy would expand during such games and nature would kick in and you would find yourself sliding down the school banister more often than you used to, for other reasons than just the fun of it. Or in the bath or in bed you would find yourself giving your willy a good rub for reasons you did not understand. It was getting so bad with boys sliding down the staircase banister at school that the headmaster Mr Lee got the school caretaker to put a stud in the banister at the bottom and as you can imagine it soon put a stop to that unless you wanted your balls ripping off. Sometimes you would pluck up the courage to ask bigger boys questions about sex and other related activities and there were always rumours going around school about such activities as touching your willy making hairs grow on the palms of your hand or having an adverse affect on your eye sight and I did often wonder about the boys in our school who wore glasses and especially one who wore those thick bottle lens glasses. The story that sticks in my mind was that if you did play with your ding-a-ling it would drop off. I can say here and now that all the stories I heard were totally untrue as I disproved them one by one on many occasions in my younger years. Boys of course always like to talk about sex in one form or another and at all ages, even the school infant years, as it is part of the young enquiring mind and it was always more intriguing because grown ups would never tell you anything about it, or worse, they would just give you a clout for asking. For instance I remember during dance class in juniors when the boys would have to strip off to their underpants and vests and girls would have to strip off to knickers and vest and we would be forced to prance about the school hall like little garden fairies, dancing to daft music that our dance teacher Miss Lightfoot would put on the record player. And yes, Miss Lightfoot was her real name. I have to give Miss Lightfoot credit though because she would always enthusiastically enter into the spirit of things and join in with us and would dress up in this little tight black leotard number and black fish net tights and she was a real good looking woman. She also had a box like a monkey's fist and all us boys would giggle in excitement whilst giving her a good look over for reasons then we didn't really understand. It was also very curious how the headmaster Mr Lee always found some excuse to be in that school hall watching and we all guessed he was 'perving' on Miss Lightfoot and who could blame him? He would stand there pretending to be artistically amused with his hands in his pockets and believe me he seemed to have very deep pockets and Frankie Callis swore blind that Mr Lee was playing pocket billiards as he watched the gorgeous Miss Lightfoot strutting her stuff with her arms and her hot legs being splayed in all directions.

In later years I remember discussing girls and sex with my mate Terry Cox who seemed to know more about it than most of us in the gang. I suppose that was because he had grown-up brothers who used to make him go to bed early or give him half a crown to go out if they had a girlfriend in the house. Terry told us how he would often sneak downstairs and listen at the living room door to all the heavy breathing and wrestling taking place on the couch. He made no bones about the fact that pulling your plonker was quite normal and very pleasurable though as you got older he warned it could be messy. Having not got to the messy age I did ask Terry to elaborate about the messy part and all he could tell us was that he had heard his mother talking to his grown up sister about the state of the sheets on his big brother's bed. We all looked at each other and after some more intense discussions on the subject it became clear no one seemed to know much more about the messy phase or why there should be a messy phase at all. I could not help thinking at the time what a load of mucking about this sex business was and the lengths grown ups would go to keep it a secret. Although I was learning stuff about sex none of it seemed to be connected or make sense and I just didn't believe that having sex once, whatever I thought having sex meant at that time, could make a baby. I came to the conclusion that if sex made babies then you must have to do it loads of times. One time would make the arm of the baby and another time would make the legs and so on. At eight years old it made sense to me though how the body parts were transferred into a woman's stomach I was still working on but one very obvious thing did occur to me and that was, if sex was the way to putting baby parts into a woman then they had to come out of the man and passing a baby's arm out of your willy sounded painful, bloody painful. So if that was sex I decided that you could count me out, for the time being anyway.

Well Terry's confessions about his brother's bed sheets got me to thinking and as soon as I got home I closely inspected the sheets on my older brother's bed and to my surprise I found evidence of what Terry had been talking about. Lots of evidence in fact and I took to watching him more closely in my search for answers on sex and babies.

One night I must have been staring at him quite intensely and he growled at me, "What are you looking at!" If he only knew what I knew I thought to myself and you better not pick on me anymore or I'll tell mum about your sheets. Isse and Frankie reported that they too had inspected the sheets on their big brothers' bed and found more fairy snot. One night we all secretly followed my oldest brother because we had heard that him and his grown-up friend Jeffrey Johnson had been spotted with some rough girls from Cholmley Street. When I say rough girls I mean the type that went all the way through the sex scale from 25 to 100 with no questions asked and without the usual resistance. After much hiding in dark doorways and behind walls we saw my brother and his friends with some girls and they took them down a back alley in Constable Street. We all ran round the other end of the ten foot and crept up the alley to listen and I could I hear the same heavy breathing and wrestling that Terry had described when listening to his big brother and girlfriend in his living room. I remember my mate Frank Callis getting all excited as we spied on them and urgently whispering to me in the dark alley all wide eyed in silence. "They're shagging. Noisy though innit?"

All the noisy goings on down that alley sounded like they were in pain and I guessed that was the baby's bits going down the pipes but I didn't want to explain to Frank what was really going on with him being so young.

The next day after a great deal of thought, I did the only decent thing a little brother could do for a big brother and told him that if he didn't give me half a crown I would tell mum. My brother always was a greedy sod and his counter offer was a threaten to black my eyes if I didn't stay shtum. Eventually I did get my half crown but not off my brother but my big sister, who being nosey, wanted to know what all the whispering was about and she told Mum. Under the circumstances I consoled myself with the thought I had acted quickly to save my brother from himself and my mum gave him a big clout round the lug hole and although it stopped him in the short term taking girls down back alleys it did seem to make his bed sheets worse. Sometimes you can't do right for doing wrong can you but I did get my half a crown.

Although Hessle Road was a rough place in my childhood years, most parents kept a strict eye on the girls in their family as did their big brothers. You often heard stories about what had happened to a boy if he went too far with a girl or even worse put her in the family way. One boy I heard of ended up in hospital after getting a good beating from the girl's brothers and her father. I never saw that boy on Hessle Road again and no doubt he had the good sense to stay well away because grudges arising out of stuff like that lasted a long time, if not a life time. Down Hessle Road in those days a girl getting pregnant was almost unheard of and a reason for a family to hang their head in shame. So you can well understand that in our initial teen years the girls had a strong tendency to keep their hands on their sixpence and their legs tightly crossed. Whilst you could get plenty of snogging done in Constable Street School playgrounds at night the action was usually swiftly cut short as soon as you tried to progress up the scale or you started the hot pressing business. The truth is that we were so young anyway and such little experience or knowledge about sex that I doubt if any of us would have known what to do anyway if things had been allowed to go all the way and all I can base that on is what happened when our little gang got their first real opportunity to put a score on the door. All I can say is that the night started like any other and after stealing a bike, stripping it and dumping the frame in Jelly Fish Bay we made our way down Hessle Road, robbing telephone boxes as we went. In those days Hessle Road had a great number of telephone boxes because no one could afford a phone in their house. They were so easy to rob in those days and you could empty one in five minutes by poking an ice lolly stick up the money return shoot. Eventually our telephone robbing round took, Frankie, me, Isse and Terry down Boulevard and we had been minding our own business trying to rob the telephone box at the corner of Chomley Street and Gordon Street when this girl who was much older than us interrupted us wanting to use the telephone box. Being naturally courteous to the fairer sex we let her use it and after instructing her into the mechanics of how to make a telephone call for nothing we hung about outside waiting for her to finish so we could rob it. To say the least she was a very good looking bird and had a real cheeky way of smiling and talking. We didn't know what it meant then but I suppose she was flirting with us and we were having fun flirting back. We could also not help noticing that she was in her senior school uniform with a very short skirt and legs like hers I often heard described by bigger boys as, "good riding thighs" though being so young and innocent I had no idea what that meant but it did ring bells. Even though we were only in juniors I have to admit that it is not just pervy grown ups that have a thing about girls in school uniforms and mini skirts but pervy young boys too. As she was talking in the phone box we crept round it and tried to look up her skirt as young boys do, giggling and laughing as we took a good ogle. She seemed very amused by our antics and came out the telephone box and sat with us on a bench close by and started talking to us and she said she was fifteen which at that time made her about three years older than us. I could see Isse had become a bit taken with her and as the night progressed he asked me to ask her to go out with him. In those days asking someone to go out with you was a serious business and a bit like getting married and it also made snogging legal if you know what I mean. Isse was somewhat hurt when she blew him out because she said she had an older boyfriend

94

and stressed that he kept her well satisfied. We asked her where he was and she said he was a galley boy fisher kid and at sea and not home for another two weeks. I don't know how the conversation got on to sex but I do know she brought it up without blinking her eye and she asked us with a cheeky smile "Have you ever done it."

"Course we have," we all piped up with total bravado and somehow and I am not sure how, she was suddenly giving us all a snog one by one. And when I say a snog, I do not mean a little peck but a full throttle open mouth smacker and tongue down the throat job that made your toes curl. We would have all been quite satisfied with carrying on the snogging but she asked us all if we wanted to go for a walk and although I could not put my finger on anything definite there was a cheeky hint of something in her voice that she had more than just a walk on her mind. We did not need asking twice and as we walked we all took turns in having a big snog and I have to say she didn't mind the pressing business and did quite a bit of pressing of her own. To quote the words always painted on the window of Jacklin's fish shop it looked like, "Frying tonight!" for all us. Then she suddenly asked all cheekily and innocently. "Where do you take girls then?"

I did think of the alleyway where I caught my brother but on second thoughts I had no wish to bump into him as he was looking for vengeance. As each of us took turns in stopping off as we walked to get a snog, the rest of us were excitedly discussing in urgent whispers where to take her and what the hell we were going to do when we got there. None of us knew how the night was to proceed but nature seemed to be urging us on to let matters take their own natural course and before we knew it the girl had led us to Division Road cemetery. I suppose given that she was going out with a fisher kid the cemetery was a natural destination with memories for both us and the girl. I have to say that although full blown excitement was in the air and loins were throbbing with high expectation, for all of us there was also a strange reluctance beginning to raise its ugly head and we started making feeble excuses to each other of why this was not such a good idea but not such a bad idea as to just go home. Before we knew and the crunch point had arrived and the girl plonked herself down on the grass in quiet spot in the middle of cemetery and laid out in her full glory on the grass waiting for her first customer so to speak, "Well come on then," she shouted over in a voice of what I can only describe as bloody eager. It threw the four of us into a bit of a panic and we found ourselves urgently whispering to each other and discussing who was going to go first. If you are thinking we were fighting over who was going to have the first pop you would be mistaken and the opposite was true. You see none of us had done it and had no idea what to do and for the first time in our short history with girls this one meant business. I mean we had all had a kiss and done the pressing stuff but never ever got any further and it was plain this girl expected nothing less than the Full Monty and suddenly she was shouting over. "I'll have the 'darky' first." Now that sounded like my cue.

"Go on then Ian." Terry egged me on all excited at the thought.

"Just a minute," I protested, "Why should I go first? You go first."

For all his alleged experience Terry was suddenly reluctant too and turned to Isse.

"Go on Isse, you go first."

"Why should I go first?" retorted Isse. "She asked for you first," he said looking me.

"Go on Ian," Terry started up again and started to give me some pointers. "Just start with twenty five, then fifty and Bob's your uncle." And suddenly they were all pushing me over in her direction.

"Alright, alright," I snapped at them, "Stop pushing

me." And slowly I made my way gingerly across to the girl tripping over twice in the dark as I went.

"Remember start with twenty-five." I could hear Terry urgently whispering after me as Frankie and Isse giggled away. I approached the girl slowly and thought I would take a gradual romantic approach with some opening patter like, "Of all the graveyards, in all the world and you have to come into mine," but before I could make my pitch she suddenly pulled me down and jumped on top of me like a mad alley cat and started almost sucking my face off with her mouth and her tongue was down my throat almost tickling my tonsils. Over her shoulder I could see the silhouette of the others watching me with eyes staring wide.

"Remember Ian, go for fifty, then seventy-five, the smelly finger job!" I could hear Terry shouting at me. Before I knew it, it all started to get quite enjoyable and I began to enter into the spirit of things and by now the girl was trying to get her hand down my trousers. I was now beginning to think I wasn't ready for this but there was no stopping her and I had to push her face off me and come up for air.

"I can't breath," I cried aloud.

"Go for seventy-five." Terry was shouting at me.

I thought fifty came before seventy-five and I didn't want to get mixed up and not stick to the right order so I stuck my hand in her blouse and squeezed the contents. I remember thinking they were all warm and soft and she seemed to go up several gears and started riving me around like a rag doll.

"Now!" Terry was shouting eagerly, "go for seventy-five!" and in the throws of passion I took Terry's advice and winced my face and cringed.

"Ehhhh!" I suddenly shouted out aloud.

"What's wrong?" Terry shouted over.

"It's all squishy," I said with a sour face but there

was no stopping now, the forces of nature and the girl was on me, wrestling and pressing herself all over me like one of those randy dogs and a lightning thought suddenly struck me. What if people got stuck together like the dogs you see shagging in the street? I had no doubt that Terry, Isse and Frankie would oblige with a bucket of water. In any case if I had any doubts now, we had both gone beyond that point of no return and she was like a wild animal and things just went on from there almost automatically and before I knew it was over and I was done if you know what I mean. The excitement suddenly left me and you are literally left with a damp squid and it was all beginning to seem like a very a bad idea. At that point in the films they usually have a fag but I was still busy trying to fight her off and eventually managed to get up and I waddled away like a penguin with my pants half up and left her to whoever was next. Having been the trailblazer the inhibitions of the other three seemed to have evaporated and Terry almost knocked me over in his excitement to get stuck in, as it were, and was eagerly pulling his trousers down on the en route and have to add that all I heard from behind me was a couple of grunts and Terry almost beat me back to the lads. "That was quick." I said at him in surprise.

"I don't mess about, Speedy Gonzales that's me," he said adjusting his pants with a big satisfied smile at a good job done.

After Terry Isse went next and then Frankie and the time spent on the job seemed to get shorter as each went up to the crease to bat. Frankie would admit later that he was not sure if he had done it right or if he had been on target but he certainly seemed to have enjoyed the experience and could not stop talking about it on the way home and we all feverishly compared notes.

We never did find out who that girl was and never saw her again despite some intense searches and the whole experience was a bit surreal. For us though it was another mile stone passed on the long and rough road of growing up and putting your first notch on the bed post is always one of the biggest milestone in anyone's life and of course it will be the one notch of the many and the one that you never forget carving.

CHAPTER NINE

It wasn't until about a year or so later that our experience in the graveyard would come back to aptly haunt us. I think it was sometime in our second year in senior school and the whole school was to have a medical. Included in the medical was a particular procedure nicknamed the "cough and drop" and on previous years I had noted that it had put the fear of God up the older boys in the school. It was called such because you would have to stand with just your underpants on and after the doctor had examined your chest and the rest of you, he would ask you to drop your underpants and cough. I am not sure to this day what the "drop" part of the nickname meant and I have no real interest in finding out even now. Suffice to say it soon became clear why the older boys had shown such fear in previous years as a very strong rumour started circling around school that the "cough and drop" was to find out if you had been having sex. I nearly swallowed my Adam's apple in panic when I heard this, as did almost all in our class. I immediately devised a plan to twag school on the day of the examination and many of us would have done so but one of the bigger boys told me that they would send the Police around to our houses and do the "cough and drop" in front of our parents.

That night we all got together in a panic and sat in a doorway down Marmaduke Street wondering what we could do.

"It's not just for sex," Terry told us all. "My brother says it is also to check if you've been wanking."

If that was the case I was in big, big trouble and so was Terry because he was a serial offender.

100

"But how can they tell?" I asked Terry in a shaky voice because he was the gang's leading light on such matters.

"When you cough your balls go up," he explained, "and if you've had sex or been playing with it they don't come down."

"Go get your torch." I said to Terry emphatically

Terry came back with his torch and we all went round the back of Marmaduke Street onto the waste ground and dropped our trousers. I coughed first and Terry gave me a good looking over. "Well?" I demanded.

Terry shook his head quite definitely. "They're not dropping," said Terry.

I coughed louder. "Have another look, have another look!" I almost pleaded with him.

Again Terry gave me the expert once over and shook his head again. "No, they're going up when you cough, but not coming down. That a sure sign."

"Just a minute," I said confused. "They can't keep going up every time I cough. I mean they have to come down sometimes."

Terry took another look with the torch and I coughed so hard I thought I was bringing a lung up.

"No," said Terry definitely, "The higher they go, the more wanking you've done."

"Oh fucking hell!" I said aloud.

Terry then inspected Isse and Frankie with the same result. At that precise moment Mr Sprigs who owned the house that backed onto the waste ground pulled up his back bedroom window and shouted at us. "What the hell's going on down there?" Stopping and explaining what we were doing outside his back bedroom window at night with our pants down and looking at each others willys with a torch somehow did not have a ring of plausibility. So under the circumstances we all pulled up our pants and ran for it but it didn't stop Mr Sprigs giving us some really curious looks over the next few weeks.

The next morning we all met up before school, we were all scared and did not know what to do. It was not so much the sex that was worrying us as we had only done it once with that girl in the graveyard and even then it was debatable if the session had lasted long enough to show up on the cough and drop scale. Yes, it was the wanking that was the issue that as worrying us. On the way to school we stopped off at the local shop near school and bought five park drive tipped cigarettes and a penny box of matches. We all stood outside the shop, puffing away and worrying along with another crowd of boys from our year also smoking and worrying about the same thing. Theories abound were thrown around by everyone but no matter how we looked at our problem there did not seem an answer. Then as if we didn't have enough problems on our minds to worry about suddenly a car screeched to a halt outside the shop and Dickey Barker the gym teacher, also known by us as Woofy Barker bolted out the car fully clad in this green track suit that he never seemed to take off and caught us all dead in the water puffing away. As a teacher he had always been an odd-bod to say the least but if anyone could lay a trap to catch us smoking it was always Woofy Barker and he took such great pleasure in his work. He also had this odd speech impediment that was a really annoying habit of punctuating every sentence with shushing noises dotted around his sentences.

"Right you lot! Shushhh. Get those fags out, shushhh, and get your backsides, shushhh, into gear and into school, shushhh." He went round every one of us stood outside the shop searching us and confiscating our fags. He looked as pleased as a spiteful pixie with the haul of fags he collected and had good reason to be. One lad he searched had brought a full carton of two hundred fags to sell at school and Woofy copped the lot, "I'll see you all later shushhhh," and announced in an ominous voice, "once I've toned up my sandshoe arm, shushhh," and he deliberately whacked the air with his hand as a taster of what we all could look forward to later that day. Woofy Barker was a fitness nut case and showed absolutely no mercy with wrongdoers and in particular he would really put his back into his swing when it came to giving the slipper to smokers and you would have a sore arse for days. He almost took a sadistic pleasure in trying to take the skin off your arse with this one special and massive sandshoe he kept special for such occasions.

From that moment on I had an awful bad feeling about the whole day and after much more intense thinking and discussion on the major problem of the day we all faced up to the fact that we had no other option but for once in our lives to be honest admit what we had been and face the music and take the consequences. Isse was in my class at school and we spent the whole morning on edge just waiting to be called for our medical and I also noticed it was not just us who seemed to be scared but the whole class had that look of impending doom on their faces. Yes, it was clear they had all been pulling their plonkers and eventually the door to the classroom opened and our names were called out from a list to go see the doctor and by now real fear was churning in my stomach. The headmaster's office had been turned into an examination room and a whole line of boys stood waiting outside in their underpants and they all had the same expression of terror on their faces. One by one they went in and came out and one boy came out crying and that set us all off worrying more, then suddenly it was my turn. The doctor did his stuff on my chest and back and then asked me to drop my underpants. He bent down and looked at my equipment and asked me to cough and I gave the feeblest cough I could.

"You'll have to do better than that lad," the doctor scowled at me. "Now cough hard!" he shouted. I coughed again. "That's better," he said and seemed to take a long time writing something down. I don't know if it was my guilty conscience but I did get the impression he told me to go rather abruptly. When it was all over we all sat impatiently in class waiting for the names of the guilty to be called again. Over the day our classes would get interrupted as certain names got called out to go back to see the doctor and fear was growing by the minute and as the boys came back we urgently questioned them on what had happened and discovered the doctor had re-called them for a re-examination. But for what we all wondered. The all of a sudden the door of our class swung open and Mr Mackay the Deputy Headmaster stormed into the room without knocking and was as customary then we all stood up as a mark of respect. Mr Mackay was a giant of a man but as thin and lanky as a rasher of streaky bacon and although at Boulevard there were teachers you could mess about, he was not one of them because he would knock your block off. He stood looking down at the whole class with a real scowl of anger on his face and looked at me directly and then at Isse. "I should've have known you two would be on the list," he growled at us and he raised a clip board. "The following go down now to the headmasters office," and he reeled off the names and I was first. "Achmed, Turner, Bunting, Eccles, Griffin, Tracy." We all stood there frozen to the spot in horror.

"Well move then!" Mr Mackay screamed at us and we bolted out the class with Mr Mackay following close behind and screaming like a sergeant major, "Quick march, quick march!"

I tried whispering to Isse but before I could get a word out Mr Mackay boomed aloud at me. "No talking Achmed! Don't be giving Turner any ideas," and we were all frog marched down the corridor at the double and into the headmaster's office, where the headmaster Mr Gillies sat waiting for us at his desk like a bubbling volcano that was ready to erupt. We all lined up in silence hardly daring to move. Although Mr Gillies was an old man with a craggy, bright blood red face covered in wrinkles and veins he was something of a legend at Boulevard for being handy with the cane. He always kept the cane bamboo stick he would whack your hands with on his desk and in full view so anyone who was getting bollocked would be mentally tortured with the certain knowledge of what was coming while he was bollocking you.

"I don't have to tell you why you are all here. Do I?" he shouted at us and when none us moved. He shouted at us again, louder this time, "Do I!"

"No Sir," we all answered in unison.

"I have to say that you rabble are a disgrace to the school," said Mr Gillies, "and whilst all the faces I see here are the usual suspects, especially you Achmed and Turner, I am particularly surprised at seeing you in this line up Bunting."

"Yes, sir," Bunting answered timidly.

"I take it Bunting, you do know why you are here." Mr Gillies demanded an answer.

Bunting was the goody-goody of the class and a bit of a teachers' pet because he always did his home work and always wore an immaculate school uniform with a school tie and was never late or ever off school. In contrast to me I held the record for never having completed a full week in school without a day off and was legend for having the personal services of the school board man, Ted Key who would come around to my house several mornings a week to get me out of bed, and if there was one thing I would never have been seen dead in, it was the school uniform. I couldn't help a smug feeling that Bunting was getting his just deserts for being the class creep. We all silently looked at Bunting and wondered how he was going to explain this one. Bunting then burst into a fit of tears but tears cut no ice with Mr Gillies and if anything it made him more angry, it was crying because he was always going on about the war and how it made men out of boys and that if fighting the Germans had been left to the likes of us we would have lost. I had to admit he had a good point there.

"Never mind the tears Bunting!" he boomed at him, "I asked you a question boy and I expect and answer. Well?"

Bunting started sniffling through his tears and we all stood with baited breath for an explanation to this one. "It's about the wanking Sir," he answered slowly.

Mr Gillies was suddenly on his feet, "What did you say boy?" he screamed aloud in outrage with veins now bulging out of his face.

"It's about the wanking sir," Bunting said again.

"It most certainly is not," Mr Gillies shouted at him. "I don't know what has put that filthy idea into your head. All of you were caught red handed by Mr Barker outside the local shop smoking."

I saw my chance here to do myself some good and get some Browny points, "But Mr Gillies," I hesitantly interrupted with pretence of fear in my voice as teachers liked you to be scared, "Bunting wasn't with us Sir. He doesn't smoke."

Bunting's sudden outburst about wanking seemed to have muddied the waters on the whole smoking issue and had thrown both Mr Gillies and Mr Mackay on to the back foot and in some confusion Mr Gillies suddenly dismissed us all and sent us back to the class without so much as a ticking off and I assumed we would have to await further developments on the wanking issue. We were all a bit confused ourselves as to what had gone on and all that day we waited with dread at the thought of having our name called out again but nothing happened and the day ended with nothing more that the four o'clock bell sounding home time. It would later transpire that the upshot of all our worry was that nothing happened and the rumour about the "cough and drop" had been no more than an old wives' tale spread by the senior boys to scare all the youngsters and it had certainly done that but what a bloody relief. That night we all got together to celebrate and after stealing four bottles of Guinness from Bev's off licence we had a sleep over in Isse's bedroom. If the whole affair with the cough and drop episode had left us psychologically scarred with an understandable reluctance to pulling your plonker. But it certainly wasn't long that night before Terry was making a tent and was up to his nocturnal routines again and started "pulling one off" under the covers. All I can say is old habits die-hard and I was definitely glad to see the end of that day.

CHAPTER TEN

Although I didn't know anybody down Hessle Road who wasn't a thief of one sort or another, I have to admit that if anyone came close to being honest it was my middle brother Graham. There was only eighteen months between his birthday and mine and people often took us for twins or just got mixed up who was who. That always came in handy for me because he would often get the blame for something I had done and since I was always up to something dodgy it was something of a relief that Graham would unwittingly often take the heat off me. We have all heard the story of the Ugly Duckling and that was me as I grew up but Graham stayed the Ugly Duck... just kidding Graham. Whilst I was always in search of a dodgy angle to make easy money, my brother Graham was the black sheep of the family and not in the least bit dodgy and had a bit of a 'Midas touch' for getting jobs out of school and so he always made his pocket money through hard work and graft and I'm even getting tired writing about it. This one time, word had spread around Hessle Road about a cut price shop that was opening on the corner of Wellstead Street. We had all watched the store being fitted out and it looked a bit too posh for Hessle Road because there were watches and all sorts of glitzy jewellery being put on display in the windows as the shop was being stocked up and the inside being fitted out. One night my brother Graham came home late and told my mum he had been working at this new shop after school helping them carry stock upstairs and cleaning up the place. The man who owned the place had given him the massive sum of five pounds for helping all evening. My mum's rant about

Graham coming in late soon subsided as he gave my mum a few quid and then toddled off to bed so he could get up early for school. How's that for a goody, goody? It was not long of course before me and my mates, Frankie, Terry and Isse decided to give the shop a good looking over. They had finished putting up all the signs at the front and it was called Peter Debbs' Discount Store and to us as little kids the front shop window looked just like a glowing chest of pirates' treasure. It was filled with gold watches, silver watches and so many types of exotic cigarette lighters you could not count them and an endless assortment of shiny, glowing baubles, bangles and beads, the like you had never seen in a shop window on Hessle Road. In another part of the window were big televisions, portable televisions and all size and manner or record players and transistor radios. Transistors were all the rage then because you could carry them with you and listen to music wherever you went as they were powered by a small battery and everybody wanted one. You could only have described the windows of Peter Debbs' Discount Store as a magpie's dream. So you could well understand that we were awestruck as we looked in and our little magpie brains were already ticking over ten to the dozen to the sound of that root of all evil, money, money, money, jingling around in our heads and how we could make some. If a Genie had come out of a bottle there and then and given us all a wish, what happened next couldn't have fitted that wish any better. A big lorry pulled up outside the shop and my brother and his schoolfriend Joey Manston came out of the shop like two little busy bees with their sleeves rolled up, quickly followed by a well-dressed old bloke puffing on a cigarette in the corner of his mouth. It transpired that this was the father of the owner Peter Debbs and was in fact the real owner Lou Debbs and they all got stuck into unloading the lorry like Trojans. The four of us stood watching box after box of radios, record players, watches, cuff links, rings, you name it, were unloaded before our eyes and taken into the shop. As my brother and Joey were unloading the lorry, they were talking to us and it wasn't long before the old bloke who owned it asked the four of us if we wanted to help and I know exactly what you are thinking, the fool. With great big beaming smiles we all jumped in and started heaving boxes of all shapes and sizes into the shop and up the stairs into a big stockroom. If we thought the shop window was full of goodies, what was piled in row upon row upstairs just took our breath away, and almost immediately the four of us were ripping open boxes at the back of the storeroom to see what was in them. The first box was full of small transistor radios in black leather cases and we were soon stuffing one each into our trousers between the legs, before we hid the boxes that we'd opened. The radios were small enough not to be noticed and all night we merrily skipped as we unloaded the rest of the lorry and had two tea breaks, fish and chips and all got a fiver each for our good nights work and a sore crutch from the radios chafing between our legs. I suppose it is a bit ungracious biting the hand that feeds you and I did feel a bit guilty. But we all soon got over it and consoled ourselves with the thought that we could make much more by simply just stealing as much we could, and it was so much less hard work. The owner was so pleased with our night's work that he asked us all to go back the next night after school and being the little hard workers we were, we were more than agreeable. On our way home that night the four of us pulled out our radios and gloated over our booty. I had never owned a portable radio before and was so excited when I turned it on and got all the strange sounds and languages of the world at the stroke of a dial. Of course my brother Graham, old honest Joe did nothing but moan about us nicking the radios, saying we were spoiling it for him and his mate and that he was going to tell my mother but he retracted the threat after we all threatened to punch his lights out.

That night I went to bed all excited and under the covers played my radio and listened to Radio Caroline with all the hits of the day blasting out from the cosy warmth under my blankets. I didn't get to sleep whilst the early hours and by the morning my battery was flat as I had fell asleep listening to it, so a new battery would be the first item on my 'shopping list' when we went back to the shop.

Before going back the following night we all took a look around the back of the shop. We noticed that it had toilet windows on the ground floor and upstairs, with a drop that would nicely take anything being tossed from the windows, straight into some well placed dustbins. It was perfect. We quickly put the bins in position and padded them out with cardboard in the bottom, to break the fall of any stuff we threw out.

A little later we all returned to the shop and Lou the owner told us he was expecting two big lorries and asked, "Would it be ok if you all worked late?" We told him that our parents wouldn't mind and he said he would give us extra if we could empty the lorries by eleven o'clock and get all the stuff into the stockroom upstairs. We could hardly help rubbing our greedy little hands together and were more than happy to oblige but obviously we couldn't guarantee it would be all going into his stockroom. Whilst we waited for the lorries he told us to go upstairs and tidy up and we were off our starting blocks before the gun went off. We bolted upstairs and of course it wasn't long before we were opening boxes and tossing stuff out the windows and into the dustbins outside at the back. We just couldn't believe our eyes as we opened box after box, it was like we were the forty thieves in Aladdin's cave. Small sparkly stuff always has an attraction for kids and grown-ups alike because it looks expensive so we concentrated on watches, cigarette lighters and loads and loads and loads of cuff links in real posh cases. We guessed that Isse Turner, 'the pawn' would like stuff that sparkled and also we could get a lot more small stuff in the dustbins than big stuff like radios. With stuff flying out the upstairs back toilet window like there was no tomorrow we soon filled the dustbins. But then Terry looked outside and reported back in a bit of a panic.

"We've filled the dustbins and there's stuff all over the back way," he warned. So I pretended to go to the fish shop and pelted round the back and tucked all the stuff neatly into the dustbins and covered it up with rubbish. After a quick trip to the chip shop, I then went back to the shop.

"You're doing a grand job lads," said Lou, congratulating me as I came back carrying several bags of chips. Upstairs we all got stuck into the chips and started eagerly discussing what we were going to do with our booty. My brother Graham could not stop moaning all night being the misery guts he was and declined taking a share of the profits of our ill gotten gains. Just as we finished our chips both lorries turned up and we got stuck in with a vengeance unloading them, making a careful mental note of what would be worth nicking later as we carried endless boxes into the shop. Filled with the excitement of wanting to collect our stash from the back way we all worked our little balls off and got finished by ten o'clock and Lou paid us with eight pound notes each. In those days it was so rare for a kid to have paper money and to have eight paper pound notes plonked into your grubby little hands was a dream. Paper money just looked so nice and we all got it in one pound notes so it looked like loads and loads of money and of course it was loads of money in those days. As usual my brother being the "conscience of the world" gave us all earache all the way home and said he and Joey weren't going back to the shop because if we got caught he would get the blame because

112

he was the oldest.

"And anyway me and Joey have got another job," he said and announced the local fruit and veg shop man said they could work for him after school. My brother never did know a good thing when he saw one but at least he could be sure we wouldn't be muscling in on that one because it was too much like hard work and who wanted to nick a pound of apples or bananas anyway unless you were a monkey?

Later that night when Hessle Road had cleared, me Isse, Terry and Frankie stealthily pushed our little old rusty pram, like four midnight phantoms, the short distance from Marmaduke Street to Wellstead to collect our stash. In the dark round the back of the shop, we piled it onto the pram and had nicked so much stuff it was falling out over the sides. We all tucked our jumpers into our trousers and stuffed as much as we could down there and made our way down the back of Constable Street to avoid Hessle Road. There were always cop cars patrolling at that time of night and we knew that four little kids wearing short trousers and pushing a pram would look a bit suspicious. Luckily the gates to Constable Street School had been left open and so we quickly ducked into the dark playgrounds and huddled in the school main entrance. As we went through all the booty in the pram it was becoming clear we might have bitten off more than we could chew. "It must be worth thousands," said Terry all greedy and excited.

"But what are we going to do with it until we can get rid of it," said Isse and there lay the crux of our problem. I shared a bedroom with my brothers and so did the others, so it was a no go for any of us to hide it in any of our houses. After much discussion ranging from burying it in Division Road cemetery to even taking some of it back, the latter I hasten to add not given much consideration, Isse had a bit of a brain storm. After one of our crazy escapes at school when we had thrown about forty dustbins full of cinders from the school boilers down the stairs of the boiler room, we had all been given six of the best with a cane and made to stay after school and dig out the caretakers moped since that was where he had kept it. We had also been unaware at that time that the caretaker Mr Mellors and his deputy, we kids nicknamed Deputy Dog after the famous cartoon character, had been having a snooze at the time and we had also buried them as well. I would add that they both took a great deal of pleasure watching us getting caned in the headmaster's office. Big skinny Mr Mackay, the Deputy Head had been given the honour of pasting us that day and he really laid into us one by one, taking the stick right back over his head and letting rip with all his might and you could hear the swish of the cane going through the air. We emerged from the headmaster's office blowing wildly and shaking our hands in the air with the pain. We were both laughing and crying at the same time, as Mr Mellors and his deputy had both been stood watching us get the cane still covered from head to foot in cinder and coal dust. Mr Mellors had this massive safety pin holding up his trousers and it just looked so funny, we had had a busting fit of laughter in the headmaster's office and that was also another reason Mr Mackay had laid on the cane so hard. Though I'd add that whilst Mr Mellors and his deputy had their moment of satisfaction it did not last long because some days later we stole his moped and after a night joy riding we dumped it into Jelly Fish Bay just to top off our revenge.

Anyway, to get back to the problem in hand and Isse's idea, when we had cleaned up the boiler room we had found some nice nooks and crannies and Isse suggested that we hide the stuff there. Even though it was now well gone midnight, we knew that we could get into the boiler room through the coal chute in the playground. And as it was all back-streets to Boulevard School from Constable Street, there was virtually no risk of bumping into any coppers. It took about ten minutes for the four of us to brothel creep our way through the quiet streets to Boulevard School gates. Isse and me climbed up onto the gates and carefully pulled over the pram with Terry and Frankie pushing up on the other side. Terry and Frankie then climbed over and we were in the playground. We pulled up the manhole cover to the boiler room coal chute and Isse and me slid down the chute. Next, Terry and Frankie sent down the chute all the stuff we had nicked and then they slid down into the boiler room as well. We left some of the stuff in the pram so we could flog it the next day at Turner's pawn shop. In the boiler room we stumbled around in the dark and eventually found the light switch. When we switched on the light we got the shock of our lives as we stared at each other because we were all covered in black coal dust and looked like the Black and White Minstrels. At the back of the boiler we found a real nice hidey place that we were sure no one would find and stuffed our treasure in there. It was really warm and snug in the boiler house. We could well understand why Mr Mellors and his deputy had turned it into something of a retreat to get away from us mad kids in the playground above. They had really sorted it out into a nice snug little home from home with two armchairs, all thread bare and torn, and a small table. In the corner they had kettle, tea and sugar and two big white mucky tin mugs. After having a good root around we all sat down and Isse put on Mr Mellor's scruffy old coat, muffler and flat cap and started taking him off and we all started to laugh. Mr Mellors had left some cheese sandwiches in his lunch box and Terry put on the kettle and we all had a cup of tea and a cheese sandwich, then had a rake about in an old desk which was down there. It was full of Mr Mellor's stash of dirty books and a half-used bottle of olive oil.

"What's the olive oil for?" Isse asked laughing. "Do you think Mr Mellors is 'reaming' out Deputy Dog."

"No," said Terry confidently. "Olive oil is good for wanking." And if anyone should know it was Terry because as I have explained previously Terry was our resident expert on stuff like that.

"How would you know?" I teased him laughing.

"My brother takes it to sea with him," said Terry, "I've seen it when I've been through his kit bag and he has dirty books as well. All the fisher kids do."

We all sat there going through them and laughing at what a dirty old bastard Mellors was. He had always been a figure of fun in the school and we took every opportunity to take the piss out of him. There was a rumour at school that had started as a joke that Mellors and his deputy would often disappear down into the boiler room to wank themselves stupid. Well we all knew the truth now and it seemed that he and his deputy were a couple of blokes who took their wanking seriously. He had also left a spare pipe and his tobacco pouch, so I lit the pipe and we all passed it around having a puff. We were all coughing our lungs up and left wondering how anybody could smoke that shit. We put everything back where it had been and sneaked out the way we had come in and were even blacker by the time we climbed back over the school gates. We pushed the pram back down Boulevard and split up to go home and what stuff we had kept back we shared out to sell the next day.

The next morning we all met up outside of school and after going into class and getting our attendance mark we scarpered after morning assembly. Lots of kids used to go twagging in those days. Twagging meant going truant and not going to school at all and that usually meant you got Mr Key, the school attendance officer, either knocking on your door or chasing you around the streets on his moped. I mean that could be fun in itself and on many occasions I had given him the run around just for the fun of the chase. But the downside was that after so many absences from school, you got sent to juvenile court and your parents would be fined at least thirty-bob, and thirty-bob was a lot in those days, which meant a good pasting from your parents as well. If you pushed your luck even more the crusty old upper class twit magistrates would not hesitate to send you to Borstal or the local detention centre. It did not take a rocket scientist to work out a dodge around twagging though. What we used to do was go to school and get our attendance mark. Then, after assembly, when we should have gone to a different teacher other than our own form master for different subjects, because that teacher didn't know who was at school and who was not, we simply sneaked out of school and no one was the wiser.

Isse Turner, the pawnbroker on Hessle Road was a great big fat bloke with a beard and always wore one of those Jewish scull caps. He was a wily old bugger and would never show any expression as he inspected whatever it was you had brought him and never asked you any questions about where it had come from. Of course he was not daft and he knew the stuff was nicked because where else would four little scruffy kids get a haul of watches, rings, and plated fag lighters still in their cases. We piled our stuff on the counter in his back room and he gave us a curious look over the top of his glasses.

"Mmmmm," he mumbled aloud, as he thoughtfully and carefully started to inspect various items with one of those one-eyed jewellers' glasses. He looked at us again from across the counter and after a long pause of thought said. "How much do you want?"

Well of course as little kids we had no idea what it was worth but our Isse quickly piped up. "It's all new and still in the boxes. What you offering?"

"Forty pounds the lot," Isse Turner replied quickly, "take it or leave it."

"Fifty!" our Isse demanded.

"Forty-five and that's my last offer." Isse Turner

snapped back.

The other three of us almost feinted at the words, forty-five. That was forty-five lovely crispy pound notes and we still had loads more other stuff left and loads more yet to nick. Isse looked at us for approval.

"What do you think?"

We all automatically nodded and Isse spit on his hand and slapped Isse Turner's hand and the deal was done. Isse Turner scooped all the stuff off the counter and took it into a back room and two minutes later came out with a wad of notes in his hand and we watched dumbstruck and wide-eyed as one by one he slapped each note on the counter in front of us and slowly counted it out aloud. "Five, ten, fifteen, twenty," and so on until he got to forty-five. As the last note hit the counter Isse snatched them up.

"Nice doing business with you," and with that we were quickly outside greedily holding out our hands and sharing the money out. That night we were back at the shop and had decided not to steal any more stuff until we had got rid of what we had hidden in the boiler house. Upstairs in the store room we tidied up and hid all the empty boxes we had riffled of their contents and threw the cardboard out of the back toilet window and then squeezed it into dustbins later, after we had left to go home. We all supposed there was just so much stock in the shop and upstairs that no one would miss the stuff we had nicked because the whole place was full up to the gunnels and that's exactly how it panned out. As the shop opened and took on grown-up staff to work in the shop down stairs, we soon found that we had competitors. One night we were all behind a pile of boxes upstairs and two of the new women staff had sneaked upstairs and we could hear them whispering and tearing open boxes. As we peaked over the shelves the two women were stuffing watches and fag lighters down their knickers.

"The thieving bastards," Isse whispered aloud.

It didn't last long though because Peter Debbs, the other owner liked to sky-lark about with the girls in the shop. He liked to 'play about' and 'wrestle' with them and we were also sure he was just using any excuse to have a good old fashioned feel as well. One night he just jumped on one of the girls out of the blue and started play fighting with her. And to say the least she did not look happy because as he roughed her up watches and lighters began falling down the legs of her trousers in full view of everyone. And because we were little kids we were all sent home straight away so we didn't witness 'horrible things'. We all thought Pete would call the coppers but surprise, surprise there she was the next night happily serving behind the counter and we soon found out why. We were upstairs one night moving stock on the first floor and could hear people fumbling around upstairs in the attic stock room. When we sneaked up to take a look, all we could see was two pairs of legs sticking out from under one of the racks at the back, with one pair of legs with knickers and tights around her ankles. Whoever it was, they were having a right old session and we all guessed it was Pete getting some compensation off the girl for nicking his stock. Our four little heads were poked over the top of the attic stairs watching Peter giving the female shop assistants a right old seeing to. We were all giggling and trying not to laugh out loud and just fascinated like most kids of our age would be with catching grown-ups red handed in shagging mode. It would not be the last time we caught grown-ups going into the attic stock room for a shag. As the weeks passed no end of staff would sneak off upstairs for a shag and staff were always leaving and almost every week some new girls would start working at the shop and inevitably they would end up horizontal on the attic store room floor with their knickers round their ankles with either Peter or some other male staff member heaving away on top of them with our

119

little bulging eyes secretly watching them. Pete Debbs thought he was God's gift to women and was always chatting up the girls in the shop and being suggestive. He was only young and I suppose he could be described as handsome because all the girls who worked in the shop seemed to fancy him. He was also stinking rich and drove this cool ice blue two-seater Triumph Spitfire sports car that was his pride and joy. Every Saturday he would get us to wash and vacuum it inside and we couldn't resist going through the dashboard glove boxes to see if there was anything worth nicking. He always had a stash of rubber johnies in the front and you could always tell if he had been shagging in it because there was loose change all over the floor. One day we even found a pair of knickers and a bra stuffed into the dashboard glove box and when we gave them to him he just started laughing. He was always having a joke with us about the girls in the shop and promised that he would get one of the girls to take us upstairs to show us the ropes but never did because he was too busy bonking them all himself.

Even worse than Peter for trips into the attic with female shag-bags was Fat Larry, the big fat van driver and store man. We used to call him 'Larry the Loafer' because the fat sod was always loafing about when he was not shagging in the attic. We had our suspicions too that Larry was stealing more stuff than all of us put together. We could all see that boxes of stuff were going missing out the stock room every day and Larry was just getting greedy and would spoil it for us all. He was nicking just too much stuff for it not to be noticed and I hit on the idea of how we could nick loads of stuff and get some Brownie points with the two owners of the shop, Peter and Lou. Fat Larry the Loafer was no friend of ours and would take every opportunity to put the boot in about us with Pete. We were cramping Larry's style because we mostly worked upstairs in the stock room after school and so whenever Larry came upstairs to nick stuff we would be there and he would angrily retreat back into the shop, swearing and cursing,

"Those lazy little bastards are just fucking around upstairs Peter, they want sacking," he would shout at the top of voice. Fortunately for us Peter never took much notice of him and would come upstairs.

"Don't worry about him," he would say knowingly, "his day is coming. He thinks I'm daft."

We all got the impression that Pete either knew what Fat Larry was up to or pissed off because he was getting his leg over more than his fair share of the girls and leaving Pete with sloppy seconds. Either way his days of bullying us and muscling in on our nice little earner were numbered and with a mischievous little plan brewing away in my head I felt sure that I could help speed up Larry's exit from the shop and at the same time increase our nicking turnover in the short term.

As relatively poor kids living on Hessle Road, you had to learn quickly to survive. In those days there were very few second chances, if you got caught thieving you would be quickly carted off to borstal for the standard three years and all of us knew plenty of local kids who met that end. If we had learned anything about life, it was the survival of the fittest and that it was a 'dog eat dog' world. We didn't see ourselves as thieves, more little businessmen and good businessman after all have to turn adversity into triumph and take advantage of the market and if that meant disposing of the opposition, in this case Fat Larry the loafer, by whatever underhand means were at hand, we would prove ourselves more than mischievous enough to be up to the task.

The dangerous thing about Fat Larry was that he was a thick bastard who thought he was clever and that is always a dangerous combination. He struck me as the type of bloke, who if he got caught would always try to take others down with him. Whilst he suspected that we were nicking stuff, it was obvious that he was - and nicking so much stuff from the shop that it was a foregone conclusion that he was going to get caught. He also had the keys to the van and we knew he was filling it with stuff on Saturday, then coming back on the night, driving the van to his house and emptying it, then taking the van back. Either way I guessed we didn't have much time to make hay whilst the sun shone. What I thought was, we could easily nick as much stuff as we could and tip Pete off so that Fat Larry was caught red-handed and that way he would take the can for the lot and we would be Pete's blue eyed boys.

On Saturday night the shop always closed at about five o'clock so the grown ups could go early and get ready for their weekly night of getting pissed down Hessle Road. After we got our wages we bought a load of bottles of mild beer and goodies from Bev's off license and me, Terry and Isse went round to Frankie's to get pissed and watch Steptoe and Son. It was about the best thing on television in those days and no one missed it because it was so funny. Frankie's Dad and big brother Ernie were home from sea and out on the piss so we had the house to ourselves. By nine o'clock we were all just about drunk and I put my plan to the lads. They thought about it for a few moments then all of a sudden we all started laughing like little drunken hyenas.

"If Fat Larry finds out," said Terry, "he'll kill us."

"The bigger they are, the harder they fall," I answered with a drunken smile of bravado.

"Anyway," said Frankie with the same bravado, "there's four us and he's a fat bastard."

CHAPTER ELEVEN

So the trap to stitch up Fat Larry was set. That week at the shop, if it wasn't nailed down we nicked it and by the Friday night we had nicked so much stuff that the school boiler room was full and so were our outside toilet false roofs. You name it, everywhere was full to overflowing. We all decided to give Fat Larry enough to rope to hang him self and told Pete we would be playing foot ball for school on Saturday and so couldn't make it in. We knew that with us out of the way Fat Larry would fill the van up to the gunnels. We pitched ourselves in hiding place down a back alley down Wellstead Street and watched all day Fat Larry dodging out the back tossing box after box into the van. He looked absolutely knackered as we watched him leave at five o'clock and it had probably been the hardest day's work of his life. We decided to drop in on the shop and got all made up for the part carrying our little football bags to pretend we had just come from the match.

"Now then lads," said Pete greeting us with s smile, "I hope you won?"

"Of course we did," I lied confidently. "Five nil. I got a hat trick. Din't I Isse?" Well if you're going to lie you might as well come out looking good.

Isse rolled his eyes and mumbled. "Yeah, a hat trick."

Now I would cast the bait. "Did anyone find my watch?" I asked innocently.

"Not seen anything," said Pete, "any idea where you might have lost it."

"Oh, I... think... I... lost... it... in... the... back... of... the... van... when... I... was... helping... Larry. Didn't... I...

Isse?" For some reason I was now talking like a real bad actor.

"Oh.Yes." Isse backed me like an equally bad actor reading lines, "Oh, Yes. It… was… definitely… in… the… van."

"Oh.Yes. It was in the van," Terry jumped in, "I remember because you said on the way home. Oh look I've lost my watch in the van." And he turned Frankie, "Didn't he Frank?"

"Yes. Hi. Remember too," said Frankie over doing it on the H's, " Hian saying that about losing hit hin the van."

"Well it sounds like it might be in the van," said Pete. "Well let's go have a look," and with that he pulled out a bunch keys and we were all walking to the ten foot at the back of the shop. As Pete pushed the keys into the van's back door we were all looking at each other and suddenly the doors were open and Pete just stood looking at the untidy mountain of boxes thrown into the back.

"Oh,"said Frankie in a wooden voice. "Hit looks like Larry has loaded hup for tonight's delivery."

"What delivery?" Pete shouted at him.

And in an Oscar winning act of naivety I announced. "Larry comes back about ten every Saturday night and takes the van. "Probably saves him a job on Monday."

The penny dropped real quick with Pete, "Oh does he now," he said bubbling over. "Ten o'clock you say?"

"Yeah," Terry joined in, "we've seen him a couple Saturday's when we went to the fish shop."

"Look lads," said Pete with an intense seriousness suddenly in his face. "I don't want you to say anything about this."

"No we won't Pete," we all piped up in an innocent chorus. With that Pete pulled a roll of notes out of his pocket and peeled off a tenner and gave it to me.

"You've done me a good favour here lads. Go treat yourselves and get off home," and remember he shouted after us, "not a word."

The tenner was an added bonus we didn't expect and after buying two ounces of mint imperials to crack it open we shared the change and the mint imperials. That night we sneaked the back way down Wellstead Street about ten o'clock to see the balloon go up and hid down a nearby alley to await events. We didn't have to wait too long before Fat Larry the loafer turned up on an old crock of a push bike with no lights. He artfully looked around for a second and then opened the back of the van and put his bike in the back. He was just backing out the van when blue lights galore screeched up from back and front and penned the van in. It was like watching Elliot Ness and The Untouchables as the coppers piled round the van door like a rugby scrum and Fat Larry was pulled kicking and screaming from the driver's seat. If we thought Fat Larry was going to go easy we were in for a real shock, as although there were six coppers struggling with Fat Larry suddenly they were being tossed around in all directions like rag dolls as Fat Larry fought back. To our surprise and not a little consternation, Fat Larry laid three of them out cold on the road and another he threw over the top of the van. It took another load of coppers to climb out of the second Police van and pile into him with truncheons flying at his head to rescue the first lot and still Fat Larry was on his feet riving them back and forth across the road.

It was about ten minutes before it was over and another two coppers were laid out cold to add the other three. By the time they had got Fat Larry down he was still growling and swearing at them like a banshee and it was clear they knew they had a tiger by the tail. Although five coppers were sat on Fat Larry it took the help of another three to get his hands up his back and cuff him and he was still fighting every step of the way like a mad bull Elephant. It took all of them to lift him and he was still lashing out with his feet and head as they threw him in the back of a meat wagon and slammed the door shut with great bellows of relief. Even after all that the van was rocking in the road as inside Fat Larry pounded and screamed from inside and we looked at each other and swallowed hard and I could see they were having belated doubts about the plan. "Fucking 'ell!" I remember saying aloud.

"If he find out it was us," said Isse almost awestruck, "we're dead meat."

"You and your big ideas Ian," said Terry in a subdued voice.

"Don't worry eh Ian," Frankie said all sarcastic. "The bigger they are, the harder they fall."

On the Monday Pete told us not to worry and that Fat Larry had been up in court and because he mashed up about ten coppers he had been remanded in custody until further notice as it were. I can't tell you what a relief that was for all of us although Pete assured us that Fat Larry did not know it was us that had bubbled him. It was though somewhat of a worry that Fat Larry had told the coppers that he knew someone in the shop had spragged him up and when he got out he would be looking to even up the score card. After that we watched the Hull Daily Mail for the next few months like hawks waiting for his case to come up. When eventually it did we needn't have worried because after the judge gave Fat Larry two years in clink he somehow managed to jump out the dock after laying out the two prison guards on either side of him and put the Judge in hospital for a month. None of this of course helped his case and he ended up with another two years on his sentence for duffing up the judge. We all worked out that we would have grown up and left school by the time he got out and Terry suggested we could always shoot him if he came after us and weigh him down with some concrete wellies and dump him in Jelly Fish bay with all those bikes we had nicked. Being full of shit is part of growing up but like the four musketeers we all shook on it and swore an eternal oath to do Fat Larry in if he ever came after us. You are probably thinking how stupid it is to write about Fat Larry and us putting him in the clink as he might well read this book. But Fat Larry was about forty years old then and I was about thirteen. As I am now fifty-six as I write this, it doesn't take a mathematician to work out that if he is still alive, Fat Larry will be about eighty-three now. And with all the fags that he put away, will either be pushing up daisies or gasping for his last breath in some shitty residential home with a wet incontinence pad.

The Fat Larry affair had shook us all up a lot because after seeing what he had done to all those coppers we had been naturally a bit concerned about what he would do to us if he got out and found it was us that had set him up. It had been a close shave and a close shave too many and after about five months working at the shop after school and on a Saturday, one way or another we were all getting a bit stale and bored with it. We were still making a tonne of money nicking and selling the stuff to Isse Turner. But I suppose the crunch came after we had nicked a particularly big haul of stuff and planted it in our hidey hole in the school boiler house and one day we turned up at school and the old coal boiler was being ripped out and converted to gas. As if that wasn't bad enough they had sealed up the coal manhole and we had no way of getting in to retrieve our ill gotten gains. Even after the gas conversion had been done we never got the chance to find out what happened to our stash in the boiler house until some weeks later. We were having a music festival at the school and the teachers all turned up in their best bib and tucker because the Lord Mayor was coming. We were all singing away in the assembly hall and raising the roof to the Dambusters, "We who are young for ever...!" when Isse suddenly nudged me and nodded in the direction of Mr Mellors and Deputy Dog, who were all togged up in their Sunday best. I have to say that Mr Mellors was the sort of bloke that could dress up in a million pound Saville Row suite and somehow he would still look like a good wash would kill him. Isse was by this time furiously nudging me more and leaned over and whispered, "Look at his cuffs!" and there on both their cuffs sparkling in the morning sunshine coming through the hall window, were our cuff links decorating both their shirt cuffs. When we looked even closer we saw they were also both wearing brand new gold watches. It then became patently obvious as we looked around the assembly that all the teachers including Mr Mackay, the deputy head and the headmaster Mr Gillies were all wearing our nicked cuff links. Later on that day at playtime our form master Mr Stathers was on playground duty and lit a fag with one of our lighters. Mr Stathers was always good for a laugh and so was very approachable.

"That's a nice lighter sir," I said greasing around him.

He very accommodatingly took it out and allowed us a closer look. "Yes, it is nice isn't it," he said, "Bought it off Mr Mellors, apparently someone in his family died and he had to empty his shop." Mr Stathers flashed off his cuff links to us, "Sold me these as well and all very cheap too. In fact all the staff bought something off him."

We all stood in the playground staring at each other dumbstruck.

"That thieving bastard," I said aloud but we all laughed at the irony and at least our teachers got a good deal. But we certainly didn't find it so funny when our form master Mr Stathers told us Mr Mellors had gone on holiday to Spain with his wife after being left some money by a distant relative. We all concluded that Mellors must have made a fortune flogging all our stuff because there had been tons of it hidden behind that old boiler. For all the grief and piss taking we had given Mellors over the years and he had ended up having the last laugh on us. After we got over the shock we consoled ourselves with the thought that there was more where that came from but we were to be sadly disappointed. When we turned up at the shop on the following Saturday morning the door was locked and all the windows painted inside with white wash. Surprisingly the shop had gone bust!

Our golden goose had died and the question as to whether we had all had a hand in its demise was purely academic. The fact was we were now all reduced to scratching a living on our pocket money or selling the odd few remnants we had left at home. I sold my black transistor radio to my sister and gave my mum a watch for her birthday that I had left over. I earned a lot of brownie points off mum for that one and she took great pride in showing it off to neighbours and bragging what her wonderful son had bought her for her birthday. She was almost broken-hearted when some despicable sod stole it and she swore blind she had seen it in the window of Turner's pawn shop, but I needed the money. One of the more useless possessions I had left over from my time at the discount store was a portable battery driven record player. It only played one seven-inch vinyl record at a time that slotted in the top. It had never worked properly and continually jumped whilst it was playing but the birds liked it and always insisted I bring it round if they were babysitting as nothing aids a good snogging session than smoochy music playing in the background. Equally, there's nothing more frustrating than snogging some bird on the couch - and just as you have brought her to the boil, and past the point of no return, and you know yet another notch is going on your headboard - when your stride is interrupted in the hot phase by Fleetwood Mac's Albatross stuttering in the background and you have to dismount to switch it off. By the time you're trying to get back on top the bird has recovered from the throws of passion and her moment of weakness has passed and you are on your bike and out the door for trying it on. Yes, the record player definitely had to go but if I was going to sell it I would need a real mug and that is where Radish, another hapless legend of Hessle Road enters my little story.

That night we were all hanging around the street when who should turn up on a motorbike, but Brian Radford or Radish as he was known to us. At least I think it was a motorbike but it was difficult to tell through the clouds of black smoke following him and that were belching out from the back, front and sides of the contraption. Radish was a grown-up bloke and as thick as two short planks and daft as a brush to boot. He liked to hang around Marmaduke Street with two other grown-ups called Bazza and Minnie. Obviously Bazza was short for Barry but I have no idea why Minnie was nick named Minnie but he was. Bazza and Minnie were two street Romeos and thought they were God's gift to women and spent most nights in dark doorways and down back alleys with the local 'slack Alices' and would spend the next day bragging about their sexual conquests around the street. I cannot remember any of them working and I think Minnie's last job might have been the milk monitor at school but if you ever wanted any pointers on birds or sex then Bazza and Minnie were definitely the men to ask. Radish was a bit of a sad character and totally harmless to man or beast and no joking, he was about six foot five tall and so skinny he looked like one of those matchstick men you used to draw in infant school and a wet fart would have blown him over. He always liked to wear this smart silver suite with tight thin drainpipe trousers and a shirt and tie. The tie I always thought was a bit over the top for a night on the prowl down Marmaduke Street. The only people I'd seen wearing ties down Marmaduke was old man Foxy on his way to court or the coppers that had arrested him. Radish lived and died in that suit. If anyone

130

else had worn it, they would have looked like the dog's bollocks but with Radish being so tall and skinny he just looked like a pipe-cleaner. He had these massive ears and a real gargoyle face and was so ugly that he would have made the Hunchback of Notre Dame look like Brad Pitt. He also had this really strange way of talking from the back of his throat with a real deep gravel voice that always sounded so serious. He liked to hang out with Bazza and Minnie because he always held on to the hope that he could get one of their female cast-offs and was always perving around the girls in the street. The girls certainly didn't mind hanging around with Radish because he would take them in Criterion Pub and pay for the beer all night in the desperate hope that they may offer him some female favours later, in return for the booze he'd paid for. There was little chance of that though because added to the fact that Radish had little going for him in the looks department, or any other department for that matter, the last big downer for any girl was that his breath stunk worse than a blocked Benghazi sewer in a heat wave and he had a pair of big, thick, wet, soggy lips with the sucking power of an industrial grade toilet plunger. If Hessle Road lasses were anything though, they were streetwise and to avoid having their lips sucked off them by Radish they would bolt like grease lightening for home when the last bell struck "time on your beer" to avoid being ambushed for a snog as he walked them home. Oh yes, when it came to women Radish never had much luck but you have to admire a tryer and he always seemed to live in hope.

Anyway, that night Radish came bombing down the street on this death trap on wheels that Minnie had sold him for thirty bob. I thought he was deliberately going fast to show off to the girls that were out, but Radish's inconsiderate excess of speed in a residential area turned out to be simply that the motorbike didn't have any brakes. And because of this, Radish had his feet down with his

131

body desperately pulled back, his hands clinging tightly to the handle bars and with sparks and smoke coming off his steel-tipped shoes as he scraped them on the road in an effort to stop. On his face, was what I can only describe as a bulging eyed look of horror, typical of a man not in control of his immediate destiny and certain in the knowledge that death or great injury was only seconds away. Interestingly it transpired that not only did the motorbike have no brakes but the carburettor had jammed open on full throttle and generally I think it was not going to be Radish's lucky day. I don't think George Formby could have made a better entrance. He flew past like a silver streak, managed a spectacular emergency stop with the help of a lamppost and ended up wrapping himself around it. That was just outside of Stuttering Joe's house and he flew off the motorbike head first and went past us faster than a speeding bullet, as they say about Superman, before his body crashed straight into Joe's front door with a great thump. He was laid out cold in an untidy crumpled heap with his long skinny legs and arms all over the place and his head sticking through the bottom of panel of Joe's front door. Although we shouldn't have laughed, it was just like a scene out of the Keystone Cops. We all ran over just as Radish was pulling his head out of the big hole in Joe's door. We all helped him to his feet and I think he was seeing those little birds and stars that you see flying around in the cartoons when Wile E Coyote has ran into a wall chasing Road Runner.

"What happened Min?" he asked, all dazed.

"You've just crash landed Radish," said Minnie laughing. "All you needed was the leotard and the leather flying cap and I could have took you for the Human Cannonball. Do you fancy doing it again so I can get my camera?"

"How's the bike?" Radish asked trying to get up.

"Looks about as healthy as Stuttering Joe's door,"

Minnie answered, still taking the piss and with that what was left of Stuttering Joe's front door suddenly opened and Joe emerged in his string vest. He didn't look best pleased with the big dirty hole in his front door.

"What the f,f,f,f,fucking 'ell's going on!" Joe shouted at Radish.

"It's Radish," said Terry, "he crashed and put his head through your door. I think he's hurt."

We were all holding up Radish on his feet. "I think you need to go to hospital Radish," said Isse. "Don't worry we'll look after your motorbike," and he winked at me.

"N,n,n,n,never mind him!" Joe snapped back. "Look at my f,f,f,f,fucking door, ya big lanky bastard!"

By now most of the street was out and because Stuttering Joe was not the most popular bloke, they were all taking the piss and laughing.

"You lot c,c,c,can all f,f,f,f,fuck off an'll!" he started screaming at them.

"Oh get in ya mucky old bastard!" some woman shouted. "Can't you see the lad's hurt."

"Hurt! Hurt!" Joe shouted back, "Look at my f,f,f,f,fucking door ya s,s,s,s,silly cow!"

"It'll let the fucking stink out then won't it!" she shouted back. "Now fuck off back in before I lay you out."

Stuttering Joe never did himself any favours with his neighbours and had always been a bit of a serial complainer and so even when he deserved sympathy you could be certain Joe never got any. The whole street was now taking the opportunity to have a pop at Joe, so he retreated inside under the usual hail of verbal abuse. After he poked his head out again, he slammed his front door so hard that it split in half and fell off its hinges.

"Now l,l,l,l,look what you've f,f,f,f,fucking done!" he shouted at Radish.

If Isse had any thoughts we were going to have a night joyriding on Radish's motorbike, they were soon dashed as when he picked it up, the front headlight and the back wheel fell off and we all helped lift it to the side of the wall. Radish seemed to recover quite quickly after that and was on his feet inspecting the damage to his motorbike, or should I say what was left of his motorbike.

"What do you reckon Radish?" I asked him.

"I was taking Sheila for a ride," he said inspecting the damage. "I've got no chance with her now have I?"

Sheila was one of the local 'Slack Alices' I was talking about and was notoriously nicknamed locally as "Mrs Mill Street" after the Mill Street V.D. clinic in the town. The name just about said all you needed to know about Sheila because that's where you usually ended up after a night with her. Now you might think I was taking advantage of a man still in shock after an accident but I had an idea. It would help solve my immediate financial problems and hopefully help Radish smooth over his impending difficulty with "Mrs Mill Street" and not wishing to miss the opportunity I immediately started my sales pitch.

"You should buy her a present Radish," I suggested subtly. "All women like presents."

"A present?" quizzed Radish.

"Yeah," I said with a smile, "And I've got just the thing for you." And to cut a long story short, I flogged him my portable record player for five quid. I think I caught him just at the right time because he was still confused after the accident and he snapped my hand off. I was well satisfied with my five quid but unfortunately if Radish thought he was going to get into Sheila's smelly knickers that night he would be sadly disappointed. The record player was not enough of an offering to curry any favours with Sheila because she was already in bed with Minnie when Radish went round later that night after the local rag man, old man Percy had taken the remains of the motorbike home on his handcart. I can though say with

134

some confidence that Radish got his money's worth out of that record player and would wonder up and down the street blasting out the same record for months. Yes he certainly flogged the Zagar and Evans' song, "In the year 2525," to death and it became something of his theme tune down the street. It would act like a warning siren to all the girls in the street that Radish was on the loose and in search of totty. The nightly monotony of hearing Radish patrolling the street playing that damn record eventually started to drive everyone round the bend. Until one night when he was blasting away his song sitting in a shop doorway, old Jimmy came out, walked over to Radish and smashed his record player into a thousand pieces with a hammer. Even to this day when I hear that song being played on a golden oldie radio channel it always reminds me of Radish and I can't help wondering where he is today.

CHAPTER TWELVE

After the shock of finding ourselves unemployed and broke at the tender age of thirteen, it seemed at that moment in time that the horn of plenty had come to an end for us. The only thing that was left for us to do was to admit defeat and yes, take a manual job, as a paperboy. Yes, a paperboy, we had sunk to rock bottom. It seemed a drastic step to us at the time but when you are stony broke you have to swallow your pride when needs must. It didn't take long before me and my mate Terry Cox were doing a morning and evening shift, delivering papers for Walmsley's Newsagents on the corner of Boulevard. We worked five days a week for the princely sum of one pound note a week and in the words of Winston Churchill, "Never in the field of delivering papers has so little been earned by so few for so much bloody work," or words to that effect.

I had never been good at the best of times of climbing out of my pit to get up for nine o'clock to go to school. So you can imagine what a struggle it was to get up for six o'clock in the morning to tramp around the freezing cold streets with a heavy bag full of newspapers strapped to my shoulder, before poking them through endless letter boxes for the morning wage slaves to read over their bangers, bacon and beans. Sometimes it could be really funny though and me, Terry and Alfie would arrive at the shop at the crack of dawn, all half asleep and half dead and watch the steady flow of early risers coming into the shop on their way to the Hessle Road salt mines. They would come into the shop all togged up with a big dirty overcoat, flat cap and big woolly scarf wrapped around their neck and face to keep the cold out. You never saw their faces and they would stand at the counter coughing their lungs up for about fives minutes before they could get a word out and would then say to Mr Walmsley, "Morning George."

"Morning Herbert," Mr Walmsley would greet them all by their first names as one by one they toddled in for the same thing. How the hell Mr Walmsley recognised them under all that clothing I'll never know.

"Twenty Capstan full strength and a paper please George." They would then feverishly rip the wrapping off the fag packet, pull out a fag, light it and suck on it like a pair of bellows and then sigh with satisfaction as they puffed out the smoke and then coughed up their guts some more.

"That first one's always the best George," was a regular refrain. They would then walk outside puffing and coughing as they went and spit out a great big slimy, green medallion on the pavement outside.

Hard work felt such a pointless task and I could not help the thought on my long cold lonely morning treks down those dark and silent streets that there had to be an easier way to make a crust. I mean you get use to a certain standard of living and we had been living high on the hog from our fiddles at the discount store but now we had been cut off at the top of our game. It was such a comedown to slog your guts out for a miserly quid a week, which had once been loose change for me and the gang. Terry too was struggling to come to terms with our fall from financial grace and was having the same depressing thoughts. We would meet up after finishing our round with Alfie, the other paper boy who was also from our street, and after pinching a bottle of flat top milk each off some doorstep, we would walk back to the shop drinking it and having a good moan and a laugh. If there was one thing about Alfie it was that you could always have a good laugh with him. He had a real weird sort of grown-up sense of humour that could be really dry and funny and that really cheered Terry and me up. Alfie fitted in really well with me and Terry because when it came to hard work he was a lazy bastard just like us. He was worse than me for loving his bed if that was possible and Ted Key, the school attendance officer was at his house so often there was a strong rumour down the street he was knocking off Alfie's mother. Alfie could be a trusting soul and if he missed his alarm he would foolishly rely on Terry and me to knock him up in the morning. But it is a dog eat dog world and the sad fact of life is that you have to look out for number one because no one else will. So sometimes if we were short of cash we would deliberately leave Alfie stinking in his pit and me and Terry would share out his round for that morning because Mr Walmsley would always give us half a crown each there and then for doing Alfie's round.

It wasn't long though before I inevitably started to fail in my regular fight with the early mornings, as the attraction of a warm cosy bed became too much to resist. Alfie would then get his own back and leave me stinking in my bed and do my round for the same cash payment. Even though we worked in a sweet shop full of fags, goodies and toys Mr Walmsley watched us all like a hawk and from the start there was so little opportunity to do a bit of honest thieving. One thing I did quickly work out though was old Mr Walmsley was a bit nervous and doddery when it came to climbing the shelf ladder to the sweet jars behind the counter. He would go really slowly and hang on for dear life if anyone ordered a bag of sweets from a jar that was on the highest shelf. In one of my flashes of brilliance I had an idea and every morning after finishing my paper round I would go back to the shop and always order the same thing, two ounces of sherbet lemons. Now I hated sherbet lemons but there was a method to my madness. The sherbet lemons' goody jar was right on the top shelf and Mr Walmsley would make real hard work of it as he gingerly climbed up the ladder like he was scaling the north face of Mount Everest. And of course that meant he would have his back to us. Well then, it was time to prepare for boarders and I would dive under the counter quicker than a ferret down a rabbit hole and fill my paper bag with a hand full of ciggies, mars bars and crisps that I could flog at school later. By the time Mr Walmsley got his feet back on terra firma he was non the wiser because I was back on the other side of the counter smiling like an angel. He would hand me my two ounces of sherbet lemons with a big sigh of relief, wipe the nervous sweat off his brow and then have to put the jar back so I got a second bite of the cherry as he went back up. You can guess that this became a regular morning ritual and I could see the terrified look on Mr Walmsley's face as I went in, pointed to the jar and ordered two ounces of sherbet lemons and he would start his slow ascent up that ladder. I think it must have been the gradual disappearance of his fag stock that aroused Mr Walmsley's suspicions because one morning after finishing my paper round, I went up to the counter for my regular order and he just stood there with a big clever smile across his face. Then, before I could say anything he turned around and took the sherbet lemons sweet jar from the bottom shelf where he had moved it to. He looked at me again with a big grin and must have thought himself so clever to have outwitted me. But as the saying goes 'never say die' that is my motto and I simply stared back at him and said casually "I think I'll have some mint humbugs for a change." Mr Walmsley's jaw dropped like a stone and he looked up at the shelves and yes, you guessed it, the mint humbugs were right on the top shelf where the sherbet lemons used to be. He gave me the dirtiest glare and grumbling under his breath he slammed up the shelf ladders and started his precarious climb as I helped myself to my usual supply of fags and goodies whilst he was struggling up the ladders.

Checkmate I think.

So whilst things were loosening up for me and I had a bit more money in my pocket, Isse it seemed had also fallen on hard times and had been reduced to looking after the school tuck shop for ten bob a week. But it wasn't long before Isse's little number with the school tuck shop went tits up because soon after Isse took it over, profits mysteriously nose-dived and it went into voluntary liquidation. We all guessed he had struck out on his own and had been embezzling the profits though he never admitted it. But when it re-opened after our history teacher Mr Hannah did an audit of the books, Isse was made redundant and we all knew for certain that he had been caught with his hand in the till. Of all of us though, Frankie had by far struck the worst deal and had sunk to the babysitting business for his sister and her Ukrainian husband Monk, who was also a fisher kid. Like most of them he was three weeks away at sea, then three days at home on the piss, big time, before he was back at sea again. Frankie got regular work at ten bob a pop with the added perk of having to change all the shitty nappies of his sister's two baby sprogs. It was regular work though, as his sister was always out on the piss or at the bingo whilst Monk was away and we would all pile into the house with a load of girls. We would drink Monk's mini bar dry of beer and spirits, play their records and generally have a right old Hessle Road kids' piss up and try it on with the girls, usually with little success I might add.

Just because we were all now solid, hardworking citizens, it didn't mean we gave up the mischief. We still went round town most nights sneaking in pictures and stealing whatever we could that wasn't nailed down and some stuff that was. We still hung around Marmaduke Street until the late hours, playing street games and generally making mayhem where we could. Although there were still plenty of people moving out of Hessle Road and lots of empty houses to ransack for left-over stuff, more and more kids were up to the same game, so the pickings in empty houses got thinner and thinner until it just wasn't worth the time anymore. By then, they had started to move people out of Marmaduke Street and board up the houses ready for demolition. But people seemed reluctant to move and despite the temptation of an inside toilet and bath with hot and cold running water on the new estates, many wanted to stay on Hessle Road. So the process of emptying Marmaduke Street seemed to go on for years and the houses that were empty would get turned into dens by local kids. We had our own den in an empty house, fully furnished with stuff out of other vacated houses or we would raid other dens and steal their stuff. Kids being kids and with their natural fascination with fire, it didn't take long for empty houses to start getting torched. Soon there was an almost nightly turnout by the fire brigade to put out some burning house. Eventually, a rival gang from Constable Street torched our den in retaliation for setting their den ablaze the night before. And no sooner did we make another den and it would go up in smoke. I remember one night the kids were setting so many empty houses on fire down Hessle Road that it felt just like bonfire night.

I suppose the way I was going it was inevitable I would sooner or later cross swords with the law. Getting caught was something I had never really thought about because getting caught was something that happened to mugs. Thinking back I suppose I should have given it more thought, especially as more and more regular faces from Hessle Road disappeared to borstal for three years. But of course when you are so young you think you are immortal and because I had been getting away with it for so long and was so good at talking my way out of tight corners around this time, I started taking more risks. It was taking just such a risk and doing some pointless stuff that brought me to have my first brush with the law and end up in the juvenile court. The Saturday night had begun so innocently and it just started with the usual four of us, me, Terry, Frankie and Isse meeting on the corner of Cholmley Street and Constable Street. It was about eight o'clock and we had decided to play some tricks on the customers coming and going from the off licence across the road. For some pointless reason we had nicked some brand new wallets from Boyes earlier in the afternoon and although we had flogged a couple we still had a bundle left. It was getting dark and we were getting bored. None of the girls we knew were babysitting and it was generally one of those nights when nothing much was doing anywhere and if we were going to have some fun, we would have to make it ourselves. Isse had one of these shiny new plastic wallets still on him and had put all his money into it. Anyway Isse hit on this idea. What if we fill it with paper so it looks nice and fat and juicy, tie some invisible fishing twine to a corner of the wallet and leave it on the pavement just outside the off licence. Terry whipped home and got some fishing twine and we padded out the wallet with paper so it looked like it was nice and full of cash and tied the fishing twine to the corner of the wallet. We then left the wallet outside the steps of the off licence and retreated to a tenfoot a few yards up from the off licence with Isse holding the twine. In the dark you could not see the fishing twine tied to the wallet and a big fat wallet looking up at you from the floor would make any unsuspecting punter leaving the off licence think all their Christmases had come at once. But of course as soon as they bent down to pick it up we would pull on the twine. As luck would have it who should be coming out of the off licence but my gormless Uncle Harold with a couple of brown paper bags full of bottles of Hull Brewery mild. I knew it would be mild because everyone down Hessle Road drank mild because it was the cheapest beer. We all started sniggering quietly as my Uncle Harold suddenly stopped dead in his tracks and

142

looked down at the floor. He stood artfully for a few seconds and trying to be casual looked around to see if anyone was watching him. He put down his bag full of beer and was just about to pick it up when another customer came out. It was none other than 'Pudding Head Pete' carrying a big tin of Guinness. Uncle Harold quickly tried to hide the wallet by putting his foot on it and then stood there all innocent, whistling away in the dark.

"Alright then Peter," asked Uncle Harold. "Just getting me breath back for a minute," continued Uncle Harold, his foot still firmly glued on top of the wallet.

"Er Harold, I'll carry one of them bags for you," said Pudding Head Pete being the Good Samaritan and almost pulled my Uncle Harold off balance as he tried to relieve him of one of his bags. "No, no, you're alright Peter," said Uncle Harold, "I'll be alright in a second or two. You get off, I'll be fine." And just as Pudding Head was about to go he noticed the wallet under Uncle Harold's foot.

"What's that?" said Pudding Head looking down.

"What?" said Uncle Harold all innocent.

"There's a wallet under your foot," said Pudding Head and he bent down to pick it up but there was no moving my Uncle Harold's foot. "Well move ya foot then!" Peter shouted at him. With that Uncle Harold quickly put down his two bags of beer bottles and pushed Pudding Head over.

"Fuck off Pudding Head, that's mine," Uncle Harold snarled at him and both Uncle Harold and Pudding bent down to get it at the same time and cracked their heads together and fell over. In no time they were both rolling around on the floor with punches being thrown wildly in all directions. "I saw it first! It's mine! Finder's fucking keepers!" Uncle Harold was shouting aloud. Watching from the safety of the tenfoot we were in stitches and then this big fat bloke and a load of customers came out the off licence to see what the commotion was about and Uncle

Harold made a spectacular dive on top of the wallet.

"He's found a wallet!" Pudding Head shouted at the top of his voice and with that the big fat bloke piled in and pulled Uncle Harold off the wallet.

"It's mine!" shouted Uncle Harold and he pulled the fat bloke over and he rolled on top of Pudding Head. Uncle Harold was on his feet in a flash and with no sign of his legendary bad back stuck a stonking left hook right on the fat bloke's nose and sent him reeling across the road. Before we knew it there was pandemonium outside the off licence as the bloke's wife and two other customers piled into the fight for the wallet. It was difficult to tell from the tenfoot but it looked like Uncle Harold was getting a good pasting but was not going down without a fight. He had laid the fat bloke out stone cold and had just knuckled his fat wife who had entered the fray again in her husband's defence. By this time the owner of the off licence was out. "If you lot don't give it a rest I'm calling the coppers!" With that, suddenly everyone seemed to come to their senses. They quietly got to their feet and brushed themselves down with the wallet just laying there in all its fat glory just waiting to be picked up. "We'll share it." The fat bloke announced.

"That sounds fair," agreed Pudding Head.

But Uncle Harold was having none of it. "Fuck you lot, I found it first," he yelled as he dived to pick it up.

"Now!" I shouted at Isse and he gave a big tug on the fishing twine and the wallet flew up the road.

"What the fuck?" shouted the fat bloke and we pulled the wallet further up the road, reeled it in and came out of hiding laughing our heads at them.

"Little bastards!" shouted the fat bloke's wife and they started after us but we were off like grease lightening down the tenfoot that came out down Boynton Street and there was no way that they would catch us.

I don't know what it was about that night but I

seemed to have a feeling something was not right with us and it was like we had lost all self-control. For some reason we emerged from the tenfoot carrying a load of stones and ran down Boynton Street just smashing every window we passed and then bolted into another black tenfoot up the road that came out on Hessle Road. We then doubled back down Marmaduke Street and sat in a shop doorway on the junction of Marmaduke Street and Boynton Street, innocently watching the crowds gather down at the other end of the street. It wasn't long before Uncle Harold came toddling up with his face all mashed in carrying what was left of his beer.

"What's going on down there, Uncle Harold?" I asked, all sweetness and light.

"Some fucking kids causing trouble and if I get my hands on 'em!" he cursed and walked off in a huff...

CHAPTER THIRTEEN

Within an hour, peace had returned to the street. The coppers had come and gone and were never interested anyway in low life, Hessle Road street business unless it was to arrest somebody for stealing from the big shops on Hessle Road or stuff like that. Yes, when it came to the troubles of ordinary Joes on Hessle Road they couldn't give a shit.

It was about nine o'clock and for us it was still early and we were still bored and for some reason that I don't even understand today, I knew the devil was in us that night. You just know, you have that feeling that something bad is going to happen but you just don't give a shit. We were sat on the doorstep of Bert Lumsden's corner shop and he had long since gone home. Bert had run the shop on the corner of Marmaduke Street for years and although it was only a small place it was always full with a steady turnover of customers who didn't know any better. It was one of those corner shops that sold almost everything from boiled ham, beer and cotton to boot polish and Persil. Most of what he sold was generally low quality stuff and he charged the absolute earth for it because in those days there were few supermarkets around and what few there were closed at five o'clock, so the likes of Bert Lumsden could more or less charge and sell what he liked. Bert was only a little bloke and had to stand on a wooden beer crate on the other side of the counter so he could see you but he was like a terrier if you wound him up and would take no shit from anybody. He had often been seen rolling about outside his shop scrapping with fisher kids who had been looking to get beer on the slate after he had said no. No one really liked Bert because everybody knew that he took the piss with his prices. His attitude was take it or leave it or fuck off. Like most of the shopkeepers who made money out of Hessle Road people he didn't live there and he always dressed like a pauper and looked like he didn't have a penny to scratch his arse with. He might have fooled a lot with that scruffy, dishevelled appearance but we always had his card marked for the greedy tight arse he was. When he closed up he would walk around the corner and then some distance down Boulevard to where he had parked his posh car so that nobody could see it. He would then throw this like doctors bag full of the day's takings into the boot and drive off towards the Anlaby Road end of Boulevard. Bert was a real hard-nosed miser and when you were buying anything in his shop, he would have a big laugh and joke with you, all friendly like, but if you came in looking for a favour or a bit of credit his face would soon change. He never gave anybody tick no matter how much your arse was hanging out your back pocket or how hungry your kids were.

"Never a borrower or a lender be," announced the famous sign that hung over his shoulder on the shop wall. Bert also never threw anything away, no matter how old it was or how likely it was to give you food poisoning. I remember one day we had bought a pork pie with a crust as hard as a tortoise shell and we had to smash it against the floor to break the crust and inside the meat was all green and rotten. We decided to take it back just for the hell of winding up the old greedy old bastard. We waited until the shop was full so we would have an audience to bad mouth him to. But if Bert was anything he was a wily old fox and was not going to let a few scruffy street kids make a monkey out of him in front of everybody. We went in all guns blazing.

"What the fuck is this?" I shouted at him indignantly. "Are you trying to poison us or what!"

147

"Yeah," Isse joined in, "we should get compensation."

"You didn't get that from here," Bert shouted back. "So don't try it on with me or you lot will get a thick ear."

"What you talking about," I snarled back at him. "We bought it a few minutes ago you lying bastard. Hey missus," I said to some woman just about to get some boiled ham, "have you seen the state of this pork pie he sold us?" and I shoved it under her nose. "I'd be careful what you buy in here." The woman almost spewed up and left the shop in a hurry leaving Bert angrily holding a freshly cut quarter of boiled ham, as one by one the shop emptied without anyone buying anything else.

"If you lot don't fuck off," he shouted at us, almost falling off his beer crate before picking up a small baseball bat he had leaning in the corner, "I'll fucking brain the lot of ya."

We all started laughing and I threw the pork pie at him and it splattered against the wall behind him and with that we all grabbed at the fruit and veg on show outside and started bombarding him with it. He came rushing outside swinging the bat around his head and chased us up the street but he didn't chase us too far because he knew the locals would be in his shop and looting it. "Don't worry," he shouted after us, "it might not be today, but I'll sort you out."

We all laughed in his face but at a safe distance. "Get back in ya stinking shop!" Frankie shouted, "and sell ya rotten meat!"

"And you lot get back in ya fucking mucky houses," he shouted back, "you're a load of tramps and so are ya mothers."

Anyway, on that fateful night, I was sat down on Bert's doorstep wondering what we were going to do and sort of banging the back of my head against the shop door.

"I'm bored," said Isse.

148

"I'm off home," said Frankie.

"Can't we come in?" I asked.

"No," said Frankie, "My old man's home and he's sleeping his afternoon session off on the couch. So he won't be going out."

Just then and for no reason at all Terry took a flying kick at Bert's shop door and it almost came open. I looked at the others and we all laughed and knew exactly what we were going to do. Seconds later, we were all kicking on the shop door and the big padlock holding it closed suddenly snapped and the door flew open. We all rushed inside and grabbed a few crates of beer, some bottles of cheap plonk and some crisps and rushed out again. Once outside we suddenly realised what we had done but then asked ourselves, why the hell were we running? There was no one about and so we hid what we had nicked round the corner and went back in.

We started by sorting through some of the food in the freezer but most of it was filthy and the freezer looked as though it had not been cleaned for years. There were some hams and all sorts of rolled meats and it just stunk with a pukey smell that almost made you want to throw up. In the corner of the freezer were some boxes of pork pies and we started throwing them at each other and before we knew it a full blown food fight had broken out and cakes, biscuits, you name it, were flying in all directions. Isse got me with a direct hit, full in the face with a pork pie and it was so hard it almost knocked me out. We grabbed a box full of apples and carrots and took them on to the land at the back of the shop where Percy the rag man kept his horse. We gave the horse the treat of its life although it would probably shit for a week after eating all Bert's baking apples. When we came back to the shop it seemed that everybody had spotted Bert's shop door open and people were coming from all directions to loot it. In half an hour the whole shop had been emptied and all that was left was the wooden beer crate Bert used to stand on.

We took our beer out onto Hessle Road and started walking into town, drinking as we went. Being so young the beer had gone straight to our heads and by the time we reached Coltman Street on our way into town we were all pissed. We were stood in the doorway of a big newsagents swigging our beer and shouting dirty stuff at the girls leaving the late shift from Smith and Nephews. We were looking in the shop window that was decked out with boxes of chocolates of every type and I just put my foot through the shop window and the whole thing came crashing down. We all helped ourselves to the chocolates with every man and his dog who passed also joining in. By this time another gang had joined us and we gave them some of our beer and had a party with the chocolates and beer in the bus shelter on the corner of Coltman Street.

What seemed like only a few minutes later, I noticed that Hessle Road had filled with kids all rifling the newsagent's shop window. Isse, Frankie and Terry looked like they were getting 'windy' about what was going on and told me that they were going home. I don't know if I was just drunker than them but as well as having the time of my life I had by this time acquired a bird and was having a right old snog and feel and I felt invincible. I never even noticed that they had gone home and ended up in town with an old mate John Gregson and a gang of his friends. I had no idea that down Hessle Road the balloon had gone up and an army of coppers were out hunting us down. I think even if I had known, I was in no state to care and by this time we were in town and creating mayhem everywhere. There were shop windows going in, cars getting smashed and the icing on the cake if you like, came when we all ended up down West Street at the back of Woolworths, hiding in a doorway. One of the gang fell over and pushed the door and to our surprise it came open. By this time we were all 'gone' and totally out of control, as we found ourselves in the strange position of being inside Woolworths at midnight. We started stuffing everything we could get our hands on into our coats and suddenly alarms were going off all over the place. So we didn't hang around and bolted across town and into the Porter Street flats. If we were now trying to hide from the coppers, no one would have ever guessed. We were on the stairs drinking beer and having a good time with girls who were as drunk as we were. We must have been making a lot of noise because all the tenants in the block were all out of their flats and shouting at us. And it wasn't long before we were fighting with them on the staircase as they chased us up the stairs to the top. We lost them on the top floor but everybody started to panic as we looked over the balcony and saw hordes of cop cars with flashing blue lights start to pull up outside. I don't know who was the first to start throwing the plant pots out of the top floor windows at the coppers below but we all joined in and bombarded them with anything we could find. Some landed on the cop cars but by good fortune looking back we didn't hit any of the coppers. We had brought all the lifts to the top floor and jammed open the door so the coppers couldn't use them and so the only way up was the stairs. We could hear an army of heavy footsteps charging up the concrete staircase and the sounds of Police radios and coppers shouting. We all bolted to the other side of the block of the flats, down the emergency stairs and ran out a two-way door. But unfortunately the coppers had gone around to the back and had one of the exits covered and were waiting to pounce as we came out. A lot of shouting and confusion followed as the coppers dived on some us. I instinctively dodged out of the way and the copper grabbing at me fell into a pile of dustbins. It must have been because we were small, fast and awkward to catch because I remember most of us managed to leave the coppers in a heap on the floor, tangled up with each other. We all ran as if a tiger was chasing us without looking back. We all took a short cut down the unlit back alleys of Hessle Road to Goulton Street and onto the pitch black paths on the side of the railway and took a body count. One of us was missing.

"I think they got Jonno," said John Gregson, panting for his breath. "He's Okay. He won't say anything."

"Are you sure?" I asked, trying to catch my breath.

"He's Okay," Greggy said again, "he won't say anything. We better split up."

I did not need telling twice and I bolted across the railway lines, hopped over the fence, down Strickland Street and then home down Marmaduke Street. I had just got through the door and into bed when there was a boom, boom, boom, on the front door. I heard my mum go down to answer it and then the commotion of coppers running up the stairs. The next thing I remember was being thrown into the back of a meat wagon where I was surprised to see the rest of the gang who had been bagged and were sat sullenly on the van benches.

I looked at Greggy, "Oh Jonno won't say anything," I said sarcastically.

I cannot remember the list of the charges but there were a lot and by morning we had all been bailed and were told that if any of us were seen associating with each before the court case we would be arrested. We all kept to our word and I didn't see any of the others until the day we came up before the juvenile court. The copper in charge told me for certain that I would be going down and so would most of the others. I don't know why but there was no fear in me, not one bit and the senior arresting copper seemed to take a dislike to me as we stood watching and said with a snarl, "You'll be going down big time if I have anything to do with it."

If he thought he was frightening me, he was wrong, I just laughed in his face and he just got more angry.

The twenty-odd of us were wheeled in to stand in a

line in front of three crusty, very upper-class fogies, who seemed to take great pleasure in looking down on us and our parents. It seemed to take ages for this big uniformed sergeant copper to read out all the charges against us. One by one the magistrates asked if we had anything to say, none of us said a word and I don't believe anybody amongst looked the least bit scared until it came to the sentencing. First up was my mate from the street, John. To my surprise they started to read other charges out against him of stuff he had been doing whilst he was out on bail. It seemed John knew he was going to get sent anyway so had taken the opportunity to go on a nicking spree, mostly of women's handbags. The old woman chair of the three magistrates looked over her horned rimmed spectacles and pronounced her sentence without batting an eyelid. "You will be going to borstal for three years. With that John made a run for the door but the big copper was on him and John was carried kicking and screaming out of the court. Suddenly as I looked down the line of us all standing there, I could feel a sudden chill of fear in the air.

The Magistrate proceeded to sentence us one by one. It was a mixture of heavy fines and three months in a detention centre. Suddenly as those who had got time were carted off the number of us in the room was suddenly down to just me. I thought I was being saved until the last and the copper who had taken a dislike to me really put the boot in with the magistrates, if he had his way I thought, I'd be joining John on a three-year stretch. To my surprise since it was my first time in juvenile court and because my mother was a widow, I was given a total of forty hours at an attendance centre, ten hours each for four charges, which were to be served four hours every Saturday morning. For the fifth charge I received a conditional discharge and for the last charge, a £1 fine. You should have seen the copper's face as I walked free from the court and the real reason for his dislike of me became much clearer.

"Don't you worry you little wog," he whispered at me, "We'll meet again."

I looked at him and then without a word winked, smiled and walked off.

I tend to learn lessons quickly and if anything had woken me up to my errant ways and where they would eventually lead me, it was the sight of John being dragged away to start his three year stretch in borstal. The look of fear on his face as he fought with the coppers had a lasting impact on me and I did change my ways from then on. I had got caught because I had been stupid, doing pointless, mad stuff with no reason or personal gain to it. Over the next few years if I learned anything from the experiences that were to come and after school the unending list of dead end jobs I did, it was this. That the only way to secure your future was through education and only that way could you escape what your background had otherwise condemned you to. I learned in my twenties, that like many youngsters of my time and background, I had wasted my school years in resentment and rebellion. For my sins I remember the one line on my school testimonial that was given to me on my last day at Boulevard High school, "Ian Achmed was rarely at school and when he was he caused nothing but trouble." I never expected much from my school but I at least expected that they would give me the same consideration as they did to most of the other pupils leaving school and tell a few lies on their leaving testimonial. A few weeks later my dreams of going into the merchant navy were further dashed by the school after they gave me yet another lousy report. I saw kids who had been much worse than I going to the merchant navy school in Gravesend and I did wonder why I had been singled out by the headmaster for such special treatment. Some years later, at the age of twenty-three I went back to Boulevard school after I had acquired nine O' levels and two A' levels at night school, just to rub the teachers' noses in it. Unfortunately most of the teachers I knew had left or retired and the headmaster was dead. So I still didn't get my moment of triumph.

I look back now and although I have achieved a good life, I know I could have achieved so much more had the penny dropped a few years earlier. Like all at my age, we all appreciate now that school is indeed the best years of your life. I know now I should have worked harder at school and perhaps my journey to where I am now would not have been such a long and rocky road. Like many kids on Hessle Road I was earmarked as a factory fodder kid with not much else as a future. But I knew that could not be right. I have made some serious mistakes along this bumpy road of life but my experiences down Hessle Road have made me what I am today. Thanks to Hessle Road I have the ability to survive and re-invent myself and not just sit about crying in my beer if something goes wrong. I learned to overcome adversity, usually with triumph, like many did down Hessle Road.

There were indeed many kids down Hessle Road like me, Terry, Isse and Frankie and many would go on to have much harsher lives than we did and some certainly did not make it this far. Today I am a freelance social worker with my own company. I like to think I am good at what I do and have worked all over the United Kingdom.

I know that Jimmy (Isse) Turner trained as a motor fitter and has had a good successful life to date. Terry Cox spent his early years after school on trawlers and later followed his dream to go "Big boating" in the Merchant Navy. I saw him recently and he told me of his ambitions to do some writing and we had a laugh over old times. Today Terry has left the sea and has his own gardening business and is a solid citizen like the rest of us. I bumped into Frankie Callis many years ago and was sad to see that he had lost an arm whilst deep sea fishing on trawlers and now worked in a bank. He never mentioned the old days and so I didn't either. I got the impression from his few brief words that he was a man in a hurry.

CHAPTER FOURTEEN

There's an old saying in working class folklore in Hull that I've heard said and read about many times, which refers to the people who lived on Hessle Road. It was that the people helped each other and that if you stole, it was fair game to steal off the likes of the shops and people richer than you but the 'Golden Rule' was that 'you never stole off your own'. Thinking back I don't really know if that was exactly true. Perhaps it was just part of the legends and the illusion that writers and romantics who have never experienced the reality, like to promote as the truth of Hessle Road. I am in no way trying to decry or belittle what Hessle Road was all about and that there was indeed a strong sense of community, but that sense of community tended to revolve around the street or particular area you lived in. The thing is I can remember many people as I grew up who had nothing at times, not even food in the house and I don't remember anybody helping them. There were some big hard families on Hessle Road and there is always safety and security in numbers and I suppose they did stick together and help each other in hard times. I can remember my coat at school being stolen twice and if you went to Madeley Street baths regularly you were almost certain to have your money stolen from your unattended clothing if you were foolish enough to leave it in the 'bunks' I knew of local men and kids who broke into other peoples' houses on Hessle Road. The gas and electric meter was the usual target, since folk has little else of value and if you had coal in the outside shed, that too would often get stolen. Hessle Road was no different really to any other working class community of that time I suppose. If you got caught stealing off your own and you were stupid enough to get caught stealing off people who were harder and stronger than you, then would indeed get a good hiding. The thieves of Hessle Road and there were plenty, generally knew who to steal off and who to leave alone. It is true that those who worked had to work hard because the simple truth was that most jobs were manual in those days and you either cut it or you were out. In the harshness of the fish processing factories predominantly or some other factory environment, there was no room for a shirker, and his workmates, never mind the foreman, wouldn't tolerate him. On the whole the majority of people who lived on Hessle Road were hard working, decent and honest people. If you fell on hard times you could usually get help of sorts if you needed money and I do remember my Mum lending neighbours money and visa versa. And as a last resort there was always Turner's Pawnshop. I remember as a very young child going to the pawnshop with my mother on numerous occasions and she would pawn her wedding ring for a week or so to put food on the table. If you had a good name with the corner shop you could always get food on the slate. But if you didn't pay up on time, your name, address and the amount you owed would be publicly displayed on a notice board outside the shop to shame you and you would never get anything on the slate again. Then if all else failed I can remember many a night when my mum would get three pennies' worth of dripping from the local butchers and we would all tuck into bread and dripping sandwiches, and even sugar sandwiches didn't taste that bad if you were hungry enough. At least with my mother being a widow we got free school meals five days a week with a pudding and usually lots of seconds. My favourite was Irish stew and mash because it had big chunks of juicy beef swimming in thick gravy and you would mix it in all together until it looked like sick and sling it down your neck. I always got a cuff round the lug-hole off the teacher for licking my plate until it was shiny clean. If it was stew, then it was always chocolate crunch and pink custard for pudding with so many second helpings that you could pig out until it came out your ears. In those days school nosh was something to look forward to and every day each meal was different. Not like the processed, additive full, fast food shit they shovel into kids at school these days and wonder why so many of them are fat or can't sit still on their arse for very long. They used to dish out little green free school meal tickets every morning in class whilst they called out the register so you could never hide from the embarrassment of getting free school nosh while the better off kids had to pay a shilling. Teachers never seemed to be aware that kids got embarrassed about such things and it was no different when the dick nurse came. We would all go to have our heads examined. Then ten minutes later the dick nurse would come back into the class and call out a few names. We all knew then who had dicks because they would come back with their heads stinking of dick lotion and that would be them excluded from kiss cats at playtime. Fortunately the piss taking because you had dicks didn't last too long because at one time or another nearly the whole class got their names called out. I remember that I got my name called out more than once. For kids like me who got free school dinners there were other perks attached to my social status. Not only did I get free meals but twice a year mum would take me shopping with a clothes voucher and use it to get me kitted out free with clothes and shoes.

But don't get me wrong, you couldn't go into a shop and get a pair of winkle-pickers and Levis, it was strictly geeky school stuff like short pants and a matching blazer. On Hessle Road you wouldn't be seen dead wearing shit like that and what was worse was that everybody would guess they were free school clothes and that you were a welfare case. I went to school with a bunch of about eight Scottish brothers off Hessle Road and they were always togged up to the nines in smart school clothes and used to get the piss taken out of them something rotten. Their mother was on her own but she always turned up at school with a new bun in the oven and pushing a pram with last year's sprog in it. Neighbours always complained about the comings and goings at their house late into the night and the local street gossips reckoned she was on the game. From the kids point of view I certainly wouldn't knock it 'cause her kids always had the latest Thunderbird toys and Jeffrey, the oldest, who was a few years above me, just loved showing off his Thunderbird Two because no one else had one because they were so expensive. He would run about the playground with a stupid International Rescue cap on with one hand zooming Thunderbird Two through the air pretending he was Virgil Tracy on a mission and he looked nothing like Virgil Tracy. I may sound just a little bit jealous here but I can assure you that I wasn't. Show-offs like Jeffrey always get their comeuppance and one day he fell over with a big crash and smashed Thunderbird Two to bits, so it was obvious from the start he couldn't fly it properly. He reckoned someone had legged him up as he ran passed them and despite being totally innocent I still got my arse whacked by the Headmaster Mr Lee after goody, goody Susan Newman, the teacher's pet, came forward and mistakenly identified me as the culprit. But me and my mates got our own back on her when we barred her from kiss cats at play time despite being a real looker and a good snogger too. It might seem mean but you have to show birds early on who is the boss or they will walk all over you.

I think the reason there has been so much written about Hessle Road is without doubt because it was the cornerstone of the fishing industry in Hull and the trawler fleet sailed out of St. Andrew's Dock which was then on

Hessle Road. Hull was then the third largest fishing port in the world, I was always taught at school and that was no small achievement that could be ignored. There were trawlers coming into port day and night and Hessle Road was awash daily with Fisher Kids who had just got their 'settlings' and would splash money about like their was no tomorrow for three days. Hessle Road was alive and the money in the pockets of the fishermen was its lifeblood and everybody who lived or worked on Hessle Road was one way or another usually working in a job related to fish. There were the big fish processing houses and the fish stands on St.Andrew's that went on for about a mile down the dock if not more, and ships chandlers, ship repairers, riggers, the list was endless.

I suppose it was very easy to be romantic about Hessle Road because of its hard seafaring history and the special harshness of those who went to sea in the small sidewinder trawlers. Writers and historians like to create myths and legends and Hessle Road's history does tick all the right boxes in this regard. It certainly has had more than its fare share of heartache and adversity but care has to be taken that outsiders who never experienced the reality of life on Hessle Road, do not unwittingly distort the true picture and turn it into something that it was not. The truth is that Hessle Road was a unique place in its way and filled with hardworking people and some very, very brave men who went to sea and many of them did not come back. In its heyday it was those men, real men, hardened people who made it what it was and their like has gone. It was the greatest injustice and ingratitude that for many of the brave men who lost their livelihoods after the collapse of the fishing industry, that it took well over thirty years of fighting for them to get financial compensation for losing their jobs. In comparison, it was noticeable that the government compensated the wealthy trawler owners almost immediately to decommission their boats.

Even in more recent times it took only a few weeks to rescue greedy bankers from the self inflicted consequences of their own insidious avarice. For many former fishermen the payout would come too late and the monies would go to their surviving family. It is a tale too often told by history about how a nation treats its real heroes because they are ordinary people.

Just as the people who made Hessle Road what it was are long gone, so consequentially whichever way you look at it, what stands as Hessle Road today, is no more than the barest of shadows of what it once was. It has to all intents and purposes gone, and gone forever.

As we are born and paint our pictures with every day that we live, experience and grow, our lives are full of many pictures that are fleeting "moments in time". I was privileged to have some of my "moments in time" down Hessle Road.

Nowadays, I often find myself waking in the middle of the night, or early on a dark winter's morning, when in a melancholy moment I will get up and find myself almost compelled to go for a drive down Hessle Road in the quiet hours. Sometimes I will stop the car across the road from the Criterion pub that's still there today. The road is so still, so silent and almost pitch dark today. It is not the same friendly place it once was in my childhood days and at that time of night it seems quite harsh and threatening and that was never true in my day. The brightness of the shop windows from my time is long gone and endless harsh shutters now run from one end of the road to the other like sinister guards in some dead zone. For a while I will just look around in the night stillness and my mind takes me back to those long gone times that will never come again.

I find it a sad place now but I suppose just like the rest of us from those special childhood days who have got old, Hessle Road too has got old. The passing of time with its constant changes has taken its toll on the old road and my time and memories of the happy and fun days I had there as a child are just phantoms now that blow in the passing breeze of time. During occasional quiet moments I swear I can almost hear the echoing voices and raucous laughter of my long gone friends being carried along in the silence. I will smile through my glazed eyes and I will long for that door to open so that I can go back, even if for just a moment, to experience one last time that friendship and endless fun I had with my childhood mates. But of course that door will never open again and all there is really left to say is, "Thank you Hessle Road for making my 'moments in time' so special."

THE END